Integrated Mathematics
Problems and worked examples

Integrated Mathematics
Problems and worked examples

C. PLUMPTON Ph.D.
(Moderator in Mathematics, University
of London School Examinations
Department. Formerly Reader in
Engineering Mathematics, Queen
Mary College, University of London)

G. M. STALEY M.Sc.,
(Head of Mathematics Department,
King Edward's School, Bath)

H. M. KENWOOD B.Sc., AFIMA
(Director of Studies, King Edward's
School, Bath)

Macmillan Education

First published 1982

Published by
MACMILLAN EDUCATION LIMITED
Houndmills Basingstoke Hampshire RG21 2XS
and London
Associated companies throughout the world

Printed in Hong Kong

British Library Cataloguing in Publication Data

Plumpton, C.
Integrated mathematics.
1. Mathematics—Examinations, questions, etc.
I. Title   II. Staley, G. M.   III. Kenwood, H. M.
510′.76   QA43

ISBN 0–333–30779–8

Contents

Preface   vi

List of symbols and notations   vii

1   Basic arithmetic manipulation   *1*

2   Mensuration   *11*

3   Sets and binary operations   *20*

4   Basic algebraic manipulation   *27*

5   Functions, graphs and elementary calculus   *36*

6   Simple geometrical properties and plane transformations   *52*

7   Matrices and their application to plane transformations   *69*

8   Scalar and vector quantities   *83*

9   Trigonometry   *90*

10   Statistics and probability   *101*

     Answers   *111*

Preface

Increasingly examination boards are introducing mainstream syllabuses integrating 'modern' mathematics with more traditional material. The purpose of this book is to provide a concise revision coursebook embodying such an integrated approach for use in preparing for either GCE O level, CSE or similar first certificate examinations in mathematics. It also provides a substantial number of practice exercises for reinforcement work throughout an examination course.

The book is linked to the recently published GCE O level textbook *Mathematics – An Integrated Approach* by H. M. Kenwood and G. M. Staley, but stands independently for use with any unified course at first examination level. As with the textbook, this book will be found especially useful for candidates for the London University Board's Syllabus B and Cambridge Syllabus D, but covers the needs of most major syllabuses now in widespread use.

The work is set out in ten sections, each of which consists of explanatory text and worked examples which are followed by questions largely drawn from recent past examination papers.

The authors wish to express their gratitude to the Examination Boards listed below for permission to use these questions:

University of London   (L)
University of Cambridge   (C)
East Anglian Examinations Board and The University of Cambridge
   Joint Examination at 16 +   (CA)
Joint Matriculation Board   (JMB)
The Associated Examining Board   (AEB)
London Regional Examining Board for questions from the former
   Middlesex Regional Examination Board   (M)
The South Western Regional Examination Board   (S)
University of Oxford   (O)

C. Plumpton, H. M. Kenwood, G. M. Staley

A list of symbols and notation

{ }   the set of
$n(A)$ the number of elements in the set A
{x: }   the set of all x such that
$\in$ is an element of
$\notin$ is not an element of
$\emptyset$ the empty (null) set
$\mathscr{E}$ the universal set
$\cup$ union
$\cap$ intersection
$\subset$ is a subset of
A' the complement of the set A
PQ   operation Q followed by operation P
$f: A \to B$ f is a function under which each element of set A has an image in set B
$f: x \mapsto y$ f is a function under which x is mapped to y
$f(x)$ the image of x under the function f
f^{-1} the inverse relation of the function f
fg the function f of the function g
–○—○–   open interval on the number line
–●—●–   closed interval on the number line
$\approx$ is approximately equal to
$\mathbf{A}^{-1}$ the inverse of the non-singular matrix $\mathbf{A}$
$\mathbf{A}^{\mathrm{T}}$ the transpose of the matrix $\mathbf{A}$
$\mathbf{a}$ the vector $\mathbf{a}$
$\overrightarrow{AB}$ the vector represented in magnitude and direction by $\overrightarrow{AB}$ [$\mathbf{AB}$ is sometimes used]
$|\mathbf{a}|$ the magnitude of $\mathbf{a}$
$|\overrightarrow{AB}|$ the magnitude of $\overrightarrow{AB}$
$P(A)$ probability of the event A
$\mathbb{N}$ the set of positive integers and zero, $\{0, 1, 2, 3, \ldots\}$
$\mathbb{Z}$ the set of integers, $\{0, \pm 1, \pm 2, \pm 3, \ldots\}$
$\mathbb{Z}^+$ the set of positive integers, $\{1, 2, 3, \ldots\}$
$\mathbb{Q}$ the set of rational numbers, $\{p/q : p \in \mathbb{Z}, q \in \mathbb{Z}^+\}$
$\mathbb{Q}^+$ the set of positive rational numbers, $\{x \in \mathbb{Q} : x > 0\}$
$\mathbb{R}$ the set of real numbers
$\mathbb{R}^+$ the set of positive real numbers, $\{x \in \mathbb{R} : x > 0\}$
$\mathbb{R}_0^+$ the set of positive real numbers and zero, $\{x \in \mathbb{R} : x \geq 0\}$

Section 1
Basic arithmetic manipulation

Fractions

When the numerator and denominator of a fraction are multiplied by the same number an equivalent fraction is produced. For example, $\dfrac{2}{3} = \dfrac{4}{6} = \dfrac{6}{9}$

$= \ldots = \dfrac{16}{24} = \ldots$

This equivalence plays an important part in the work on fractions.

Example 1: *Simplify* $\dfrac{7}{8} + \dfrac{2}{3}$.

$$\frac{7}{8} + \frac{2}{3} = \frac{21}{24} + \frac{16}{24} = \frac{37}{24} = 1\frac{13}{24} \qquad \text{(24 is the L.C.M. of 8 and 3).}$$

Example 2: *Simplify* $3\dfrac{1}{4} - 1\dfrac{5}{12}$.

$$3\frac{1}{4} - 1\frac{5}{12} = 3 - 1 + \frac{1}{4} - \frac{5}{12} = 2 + \frac{3-5}{12} = 2 - \frac{2}{12} = 2 - \frac{1}{6} = 1\frac{5}{6}.$$

Example 3: *Simplify* $2\dfrac{2}{15} \times 4\dfrac{1}{2} \times 3\dfrac{3}{4}$.

$$2\frac{2}{15} \times 4\frac{1}{2} \times 3\frac{3}{4} = \frac{\overset{8}{\cancel{32}^{4}}}{\cancel{15}_{1}} \times \frac{9}{\cancel{2}_{1}} \times \frac{\cancel{15}^{1}}{\cancel{4}_{1}} = 36.$$

Example 4: *Simplify* $7\dfrac{3}{4} \div 4\dfrac{2}{15}$.

$$7\frac{3}{4} \div 4\frac{2}{15} = \frac{\dfrac{31}{4}}{\dfrac{62}{15}} = \frac{\dfrac{31}{4} \times \dfrac{15}{62}}{\dfrac{62}{15} \times \dfrac{15}{62}} = \frac{\cancel{31}^{1}}{4} \times \frac{15}{\cancel{62}_{2}} = \frac{15}{8} = 1\frac{7}{8}.$$

The multiplicative inverse of the fraction $\frac{a}{b}$ is $\frac{b}{a}$ since $\frac{a}{b} \times \frac{b}{a} = 1$. In Example 4 the use of the multiplying factor $\frac{15}{62}$, the multiplicative inverse of $\frac{62}{15}$, reduces the denominator to 1. This justifies the rule: when dividing by a fraction invert the fraction and multiply.

Example 5: *Simplify* $\left(2\frac{2}{3} - 1\frac{1}{5}\right) \div \left(1\frac{1}{2} + 2\frac{1}{6}\right).$

$$\left(2\frac{2}{3} - 1\frac{1}{5}\right) \div \left(1\frac{1}{2} + 2\frac{1}{6}\right) = 1\frac{7}{15} \div 3\frac{2}{3} = \frac{\cancel{22}^2}{\cancel{15}_5} \times \frac{\cancel{3}^1}{\cancel{11}_1} = \frac{2}{5}.$$

Decimals

A decimal is equivalent to a fraction whose denominator is a power of 10.

Example: (a) $0{\cdot}37 = \dfrac{3}{10} + \dfrac{7}{100} = \dfrac{30+7}{100} = \dfrac{37}{100}.$

(b) $2{\cdot}013 = 2 + \dfrac{0}{10} + \dfrac{1}{100} + \dfrac{3}{1000} = 2 + \dfrac{10+3}{1000} = 2\dfrac{13}{1000}.$

The number of zeros in the denominator is equal to the number of decimal places.

To convert a fraction to a decimal may involve division of the numerator by the denominator.

Example 1: *Convert (a)* $\dfrac{3}{4}$, *(b)* $\dfrac{7}{9}$ *into decimals.*

(a) $\dfrac{3}{4} = \dfrac{3 \times 25}{4 \times 25} = \dfrac{75}{100} = 0{\cdot}75,$

(b) repeated division of 7 by 9 gives $0{\cdot}777\ldots$, i.e. the recurring decimal written as $0{\cdot}\dot{7}$.

The following examples illustrate the rules of combination for decimals, justified by the results of their fractional equivalents.

Example 2: *Simplify* $3{\cdot}14 + 6{\cdot}28.$

$$3{\cdot}14 + 6{\cdot}28 = 3\frac{14}{100} + 6\frac{28}{100} = 9\frac{42}{100} = 9{\cdot}42.$$

Example 3: *Simplify* $5 \cdot 2 - 3 \cdot 466$.

$$5 \cdot 2 - 3 \cdot 466 = 5\frac{2}{10} - 3\frac{466}{1000} = 2\frac{200 - 466}{1000} = 2 - \frac{266}{1000} = 1\frac{734}{1000} = 1 \cdot 734.$$

Example 4: *Simplify* $3 \cdot 14 \times 2 \cdot 56$.

$$3 \cdot 14 \times 2 \cdot 56 = 3\frac{14}{100} \times 2\frac{56}{100} = \frac{314}{100} \times \frac{256}{100} = \frac{80\,384}{10\,000} = 8 \cdot 0384.$$

Example 5: *Simplify* $8 \cdot 35 \div 0 \cdot 4$.

$$8 \cdot 35 \div 0 \cdot 4 = \frac{8 \cdot 35}{0 \cdot 4} = \frac{8 \cdot 35 \times 10}{0 \cdot 4 \times 10} = \frac{83 \cdot 5}{4} = 20 \cdot 875.$$

Two decimals can be compared readily, whereas fractions generally need to have the same denominator before comparison can be made.

Example 6: *Place the fractions* $\frac{7}{8}, \frac{17}{19}, \frac{13}{15}$ *in ascending order of magnitude.*

Written as decimals they are $0 \cdot 875$, $0 \cdot 89 \ldots$, $0 \cdot 8\dot{6}$ respectively, and so in ascending order they are $\frac{13}{15}, \frac{7}{8}, \frac{17}{19}$. (The L.C.M. of 8, 15 and 19 is 2280.)

Approximations: decimal places and significant figures

When quantities are measured, a degree of approximation is inevitable, the measurement being only as accurate as the measuring device. A length given as $2 \cdot 5$ m implies that it lies between $2 \cdot 45$ m and $2 \cdot 55$ m; we may assume that $2 \cdot 45 \leqslant$ the length $< 2 \cdot 55$, the right hand inequality being strict as we 'round up' if the last figure is a 5. A length measured as $2 \cdot 50$ m lies between $2 \cdot 495$ m and $2 \cdot 505$ m. The two measured lengths above were given correct to 1 and 2 decimal places (d.p.) respectively.

Example 1: *The sides of a rectangle are measured as* $2 \cdot 5\,m$ *and* $3 \cdot 4\,m$ *(1 d.p.).*

The calculated area will be $2 \cdot 5 \times 3.4\,\text{m}^2 = 8 \cdot 5\,\text{m}^2$, but the true area A is such that
$$2 \cdot 45 \times 3 \cdot 35\,\text{m}^2 \leqslant A < 2 \cdot 55 \times 3 \cdot 45\,\text{m}^2$$
$$\Rightarrow 8 \cdot 2075\,\text{m}^2 \leqslant A < 8 \cdot 7975\,\text{m}^2.$$

Although answers to problems using measured data should not be given to a greater degree of accuracy than the given data, this example illustrates the uncertainty of the 5 in the calculated area.

An approximate number may be just as informative as an accurate one. Football attendances, and population figures for cities, for example, are often given as numbers like 30 000, 1 080 000 etc; it is generally understood that these are correct to a stated number of significant figures (s.f.). If the first number is correct to 2 s.f. it is nearer to 30 000 than 29 000 or 31 000, i.e. $29\,500 \leqslant \text{number} < 30\,500$. In the earlier example the sides of the rectangle were given to 2 s.f.

Example 2: The numbers 13·047 and 0·094 673 can be written as:

(a) 13·05 (4 s.f.) and 0·094 67 (4 s.f.)
(b) 13·0 (3 s.f.) and 0·0947 (3 s.f.)
(c) 13·05 (2 d.p.) and 0·09 (2 d.p.).

Standard form

A number is in standard form when it is written in the form $A \times 10^n$, where $1 \leqslant A < 10$ and n is an integer.

It is a convenient way of recording very large and very small numbers, and highlights the number of significant figures.

Example 1: (a) The temperature of the core of the sun is approximately $1·3 \times 10^7\,°C$ (2 s.f.).
(b) $0·000\,000\,82 = 8·2 \times 10^{-7}$.

Example 2: *Simplify* $9·56 \times 10^{-3} + 4·24 \times 10^{-1}$, *giving the answer in standard form.*

$9·56 \times 10^{-3} + 4·24 \times 10^{-1} = 0·009\,56 + 0·424 = 0·433\,56 = 4·3356 \times 10^{-1}$.

Ratio and proportion

Two quantities measured in the same units may be compared by giving a ratio, or fraction. If two quantities a and b are in the ratio 3:1, then $a = 3b$, or $\dfrac{a}{b} = \dfrac{3}{1}$. Scale factors are given in this form.

Example 1: If the lengths of a car and a scale model of it are 4·25 m and 8·5 cm respectively, the ratio of their lengths is $\dfrac{425}{8·5} = \dfrac{50}{1}$, i.e. 50:1.

When one quantity is divided into a number of parts in a given ratio, the values of the parts can be evaluated by using the proportional parts.

Example 2: *Divide £750 in the ratios* 7:8:5.

As the number of parts is $(7 + 8 + 5) = 20$, the proportional parts are $\dfrac{7}{20}, \dfrac{2}{5}\left(\dfrac{8}{20}\right)$ and $\dfrac{1}{4}\left(\dfrac{5}{20}\right)$ respectively.

The shares are $\frac{7}{20} \times £750 = £262 \cdot 50$, $\frac{2}{5} \times £750 = £300$, and $£187 \cdot 50$.

Percentage, percentage increase and decrease

A percentage is a ratio expressed with a denominator of 100.

Example 1: (a) 15% of $200\,\text{kg} = \frac{15}{100} \times 200\,\text{kg} = 30\,\text{kg}$.

(b) As $\frac{3}{20} = \frac{3 \times 5}{20 \times 5} = \frac{15}{100}$, 3 is 15% of 20.

Equivalently, to change a fraction to a percentage multiply the fraction by 100.

An informative method of assessing increases and decreases in a quantity is to compare them with the initial (original) value of the quantity in the following ways:

(a) fractional increase or decrease = increase or decrease divided by original value.

(b) $\%$ increase or decrease = fractional increase or decrease $\times$ 100.

Gains, losses, errors are often given in these forms; errors are compared with the true value.

In financial transactions the original value is called the cost price (C.P.) and the new value is called the selling price (S.P.).

Example 2: *A teacher has a salary increase from £7600 to £8600. Find his percentage increase in salary to 2 significant figures.*

$$\% \text{ increase} = \frac{1000}{7600} \times 100 = 13 \ (2 \text{ s.f.}).$$

Example 3: *A man sells a house for £30 000. Find (a) his percentage gain if his actual gain is £5000, (b) the cost of the house to him if he is gaining 25 % on his outlay.*

(a) C.P. $= £25\,000 \Rightarrow \% \text{ gain} = \frac{5000}{25\,000} \times 100 = 20$.

(b) Let the C.P. be 100%; the S.P. is then 125%.

As the S.P. is £30 000, the C.P. $= \frac{100}{125} \times £30\,000 = £24\,000$.

Example 4: *If a 5 % error (on the high side) is made in measuring the side of a square, calculate the percentage error made in calculating the area.*

Let the true length, in cm, of the side of the square be x; the measured length is then $\dfrac{105}{100}x$.

$$\text{The calculated area} = \frac{105}{100} \times \frac{105}{100}x^2 = \frac{11\,025}{10\,000}x^2 = 1{\cdot}1025x^2.$$

$$\text{The error in area} = 0{\cdot}1025x^2$$

$$\Rightarrow \text{the } \% \text{ error in area} = \frac{0{\cdot}1025x^2}{x^2} \times 100 = 10{\cdot}25.$$

Simple interest

When a sum of money, called the principal, is invested at simple interest the interest is always calculated on this initial investment i.e. the interest is not added to the principal. In this case the amount of interest, I, can be calculated given the principal invested, P, the rate of interest, $R\%$, and the time, T years, using the formula $I = \dfrac{PRT}{100}$. The units of P and I are the same.

Example 1: *Calculate the simple interest gained on £200 invested at a rate of $11\frac{1}{4}\%$ per annum for a period of 3 years.*

As $P = £200, R = 11\frac{1}{4}, T = 3$, the interest I, in £, $= \cancel{200} \times \dfrac{45}{\cancel{4}_2} \times \dfrac{3}{\cancel{100}} = 67{\cdot}5.$

The simple interest is £67·50.

Example 2: *Calculate what amount of money invested at simple interest of 10% per annum for 8 months yields an interest of £50.*

As $P = \dfrac{100I}{RT}$ and $R = 10, T = \dfrac{2}{3}$ we have $P = £\dfrac{100 \times 50}{10} \times \dfrac{3}{2} = £750.$

Exercise 1.1 (Calculators should only be used to check answers)

1 Simplify:

(a) $1\dfrac{4}{9} + 3\dfrac{5}{8}$, (b) $2\dfrac{1}{7} - 1\dfrac{5}{6}$, (c) $3\dfrac{1}{9} \times 1\dfrac{1}{14}$, (d) $1\dfrac{5}{12} \div 8\dfrac{1}{2}$,

(e) $\left(\dfrac{1}{3} + \dfrac{1}{5}\right)^2$, (f) $\left(6\dfrac{1}{2} - 4\dfrac{5}{8}\right) \div \left(1\dfrac{1}{4} \times \dfrac{1}{6}\right).$

2 Add $\dfrac{5}{8}$ of £12 to $\dfrac{3}{7}$ of £14·35.

3 Calculate   (a) $6{\cdot}4 \times 3{\cdot}9$,   (b) $0{\cdot}04 \times 2{\cdot}7$,   (c) $8{\cdot}26 \div 3{\cdot}5$,   (d) $10{\cdot}416 \div 0{\cdot}7$, giving answers (i) exactly, (ii) correct to 1 decimal place, (iii) correct to 2 significant figures.

4 (a) Convert the following fractions to decimals, giving answers correct to 2 decimal places:

(i) $\dfrac{5}{12}$, (ii) $\dfrac{15}{17}$.

(b) Which of the numbers $5\frac{4}{7}$, $5\frac{5}{9}$, $5\frac{6}{11}$ is closest to $5\frac{27}{50}$?

5 Convert the following decimals to fractions in their lowest form:
(a) 0·78, (b) 1·025, (c) 0·05.

6 State which of the fractions $\frac{5}{6}$ or $\frac{21}{25}$, is the larger and by how much.

7 Calculate (a) 5% of £120, (b) $12\frac{1}{2}$% of 2 kg.

8 Calculate the percentage that (a) 28 p is of 64 p, (b) 1·8 m is of 25 m.

9 A shopkeeper buys 800 pencils for £36. If he sells them all at 6 p each, calculate (a) his profit, (b) the percentage profit on his outlay.

10 The cost of admission to a football match was increased by 16% to £1·45. Calculate the previous admission charge.

11 The engine of a car is modified so that its top speed is increased by 15% to 253 km/h. Find the previous top speed.

12 A line AB of length 10·8 m is divided by a point C such that AC:CB = 7:5. Calculate the length of AC.

13 In a bonus scheme three men are to divide £2100 in the ratio of their times served with the firm. If these times are 18 months, 2 years and 7 years, calculate their respective bonuses.

14 In manufacturing an article the costs of raw materials, labour and plant maintenance are in the ratios 5:6:2. If these costs are increased by 10%, $\frac{1}{3}$ and 25% respectively, calculate the new ratios in the form $a:b:c$, where a, b, c are integers.

15 Given that $\sqrt{2} = 1·41$ (3 s.f.), evaluate the following to 2 s.f.:
(a) $\sqrt{200}$, (b) $\sqrt{0·02}$, (c) $\sqrt{8}$, (d) $\sqrt{(2 \times 10^{-6})}$.

16 Instead of adding 3·54 and 1·86 a boy evaluates 3·45 + 1·68. Calculate his percentage error.

17 The price of a book is increased from £4·20 to £5·46. Calculate the percentage increase in price.

18 If $\frac{\pi x}{180}$ is taken as an approximation for sin $x°$, calculate the percentage error when $x = 30$. [Take $\pi = 3·14$ and give your answer to 2 s.f.].

19 If x and y are such that $0·5 \leqslant x \leqslant 1·5$ and $1·5 \leqslant y \leqslant 2·5$, calculate the maximum and minimum values of:
(a) $x + 2y$, (b) $x - y$ (c) $\frac{x}{y}$, (d) $\frac{1}{x} + \frac{1}{y}$.

20 The heights of three boys are measured, to the nearest cm, as 154 cm, 165 cm and 181 cm. Calculate, to one decimal place, the maximum percentage error in evaluating their average height.

21 Express the following numbers in standard form:
(a) 150 000, (b) 0·045, (c) 25·8 × 10⁻⁴, (d) (9 × 10⁻²)³.

22 (a) Multiply $2·7 \times 10^8$ by $0·6 \times 10^{-3}$,
(b) simplify $4·2 \times 10^{-1} - 5·6 \times 10^{-2}$, giving answers to both parts in standard form.

23 Given (a) $(0·8)^2 \times 10$, (b) $(65) \times 10^{-1}$, (c) $\frac{0·25 \times 10^{-2}}{0·4 \times 10^{-3}}$, find which is the smallest and which the largest.

24 In a test a candidate scores 48 out of 65. Give the scale factor, in its lowest terms, so that the mark can be converted to a percentage and calculate this percentage to the nearest whole number.

25 If £400 is invested at simple interest of 12% per annum for time t years, the interest is £80. Calculate the value of t.

26 A sum of money is borrowed at simple interest of $x \%$ per annum. If the loan is repaid in three years the amount paid would be £2480; if it is repaid in four years the amount would be £2640. Calculate x.

27 The cash price of a colour television is £400. The credit terms are an initial payment of £26·80 followed by 24 monthly payments of £18·80. Calculate
(a) how much extra is paid by the credit method,
(b) the equivalent rate of simple interest that the credit method represents.

28 A man walks at 4 km/h for 2 h and then at 5 km/h for a further 3 h. Find his average speed for the complete journey. If he had walked at 4 km/h for 2 km and then at 5 km/h for a further 3 km, calculate his average speed in this case.

29 A brochure advertising a three week self-drive holiday in the USA suggests a round trip of 4000 km and estimates the total driving time as 62·5 h. Calculate the estimated average speed for the journey (a) in km/h, (b) in m.p.h., given that 1 m = 1·6 km.

If the car averages 40 km per gallon and petrol costs $1·32 per gallon, calculate the cost of the petrol for the journey (i) in $, (ii) in £, if the exchange rate is £1 = $2·4.

30 A bank extracts its commission of 50 p on every hundred, or part hundred, pounds to be changed into foreign currency before converting it. If £750 is to be changed into Italian lire at a rate of £1 = L 1880 and the money then divided equally between 30 children, calculate how many lire (to the nearest 10) each child will receive.

Exercise 1.2 (Calculators should not be used in questions 1–10; only where necessary elsewhere.)

1 Calculate the value of $(2 - \frac{1}{3}) \div \frac{7}{15}$. [L]

2 Evaluate $(\frac{1}{5} + \frac{3}{7}) + (\frac{1}{5} \times \frac{3}{7})$ expressing your answer (a) as a vulgar fraction in its lowest terms, (b) as a decimal fraction, correct to two decimal places. [L]

3 (i) Express as a single fraction in its lowest terms
$$\frac{3\frac{3}{4} - 2\frac{7}{18}}{3\frac{1}{2} + 2\frac{1}{3}}.$$
(ii) Find the exact value of $4761 \div 0·023$. [O]

4 (i) Calculate $\frac{3}{4} - \frac{2}{3}$.
(ii) Calculate exactly $7·3 \times 2·1$. [AEB]

5 Find the exact value of $\dfrac{45}{0·9} + \dfrac{6.6}{0.55}$. [L]

6 Find the exact value of $\dfrac{90 \times 0·32}{0·016 \times 4·5}$. [L]

7 (i) Find the exact value of (a) $\frac{2}{3}$ of $7\frac{1}{2}$, (b) $5·9^2 - 2·1^2$.
(ii) Express £34 as a percentage of £85. [L]

8 Express each of the following as a single fraction in its lowest terms:
(i) $(2\frac{2}{3} - 1\frac{3}{4}) \div \frac{11}{16}$; (ii) $2\frac{2}{3} - (1\frac{3}{4} \div \frac{11}{16})$. [O]

9 Find the exact value of $2·6622 \div 0·87$. [L]

10 Evaluate
$$\frac{(0·04)^2 (0·8)^2}{(0·2)^4}.$$ [JMB]

11 In a survey, 25 000 people were asked which television channel they liked best. 10 000 chose ITV and 1000 said they did not have a television set.
(a) What fraction of the people asked chose ITV?
(b) What percentage of the people asked did not have a television set? [S]

12 In a local election only 80 % of the electors actually voted, and the ratio of the votes cast for the two candidates was 8 : 7. If the winning candidate secured 1624 votes more than the loser, find the total number of electors. [L]

13 (i) A car travels for $3\frac{1}{2}$ hours at an average speed of 42 km/h and then for $1\frac{1}{2}$ hours at an average speed of 62 km/h. Calculate the average speed of the car for the whole journey.

   (ii) An article is sold for £ 57·50 making a profit of 15% on the cost price. Calculate the cost price of the article. [L]

14 A road haulage firm estimated that the cost of a particular journey was £10·40 and that 30% of this was the cost of the fuel used. What was the new cost of the journey if the price of a gallon of fuel was raised from 52p to 56p? [O]

15 Calculate the simple interest on £125 for 4 years at 8% per annum. [AEB]

16 An alloy consists of three metals A, B and C in the proportions $A:B = 3:5$ and $B:C = 7:6$. Calculate the proportion $A:C$. [C]

17 £270 is divided among three prize winners in the ratio $2:3:4$. Calculate the largest share. [JMB]

18 £979 is to be divided into three parts in the proportions $1:\frac{1}{2}:\frac{1}{3}$. Calculate the value of the smallest part. [L]

19 Articles are purchased at £2·50 per 100 and sold at $3\frac{1}{2}$ p each. Calculate the profit as a percentage of the purchase price. [L]

20 By selling a car for £1600, a car dealer would lose 4% on its purchase price. Calculate the price at which he must sell the car in order to gain 5% on its purchase price. [L]

21 A dealer buys 5 tonnes of metal at £30 per tonne and an additional quantity at £37 per tonne. If the average price he pays is £32 per tonne, calculate how many tonnes he buys at the higher price. [L]

22 A new car was bought for £2000. It decreased in value by 20% in the next year and in the year after that it decreased in value by 15% of its value at the beginning of that year.
(a) What was the value of the car at the end of the two year period?
(b) By what percentage had the car decreased in value by the end of the two year period? [O]

23 When his son is born a man pays £1800 into an educational fund which pays 7% Simple Interest per annum. On his son's 14th birthday the man withdraws his investment together with the interest accrued and then pays school fees of £800. If the man re-invests the remainder with the same educational fund, calculate the amount standing to the man's credit on his son's 15th birthday. [AEB]

24 On a train journey of 117 kilometres the average speed for the first 27 kilometres is 45 km/h, and for the rest of the journey the average speed is 37·5 km/h. Calculate the uniform speed at which the train would have to travel in order to cover the whole distance in the same time. [L]

25 The speed of light is $3·00 \times 10^5$ km/s. Calculate the number of km travelled by light in 24 hours. Give your answer in the standard form $a \times 10^n$ where a is a number expressed to two decimal places lying between 1 and 10, and n is an integer. [L]

26 Given that $k = 2 \times 10^{-3}$, express $\dfrac{1}{k}$ in the form $a \times 10^n$ where $1 < a < 10$ and n is an integer. [JMB]

27 The expression $10 - \dfrac{x}{20}$ is taken as an approximation for $\sqrt{(100 - x)}$. Calculate the error in using this approximation when $x = 36$. [C]

28 The total rateable value of a Borough is £15 000 000. The general rate levied for a particular year is 88p in the £, of which 27·5p is allocated to Education. Calculate
(a) the total income from the general rate throughout the Borough,
(b) the amount allocated to Education. [L]

29 A City Treasurer estimated that the City would need a rate of 82·5p in the £ in order to provide £68 887 500 and that the cost to the rates of Family and Community Service would be 8·6p in the £. Calculate

(i) the estimated product of a penny rate,

(ii) the percentage of the rate devoted to Family and Community Service, giving the answer correct to one place of decimals.

The Government made a grant to the City equivalent to 25·2p in the £ so reducing the rate. Calculate

(iii) the amount of money granted to the city, giving the answer correct to the nearest ten thousand pounds.

A householder whose rateable value was £180 paid this reduced rate plus an extra amount for the water rate. If his *half-yearly* payment was £57·92, calculate the *annual* amount paid as a water rate. [AEB]

30 Mr Brown and Mr Jones contribute £9000 and £12 000 respectively to a business partnership. Six months later they are joined by a third man Mr Smith who contributes £6000 to the partnership. Of the first year's profits, Mr Brown takes a salary of £3000 for his services as manager and Mr Jones takes a salary of £1500 for his services as assistant manager. Of the profits which remain, 10% are put into a reserve fund. The profits which then remain are divided amongst Mr Brown, Mr Jones and Mr Smith in proportion to the capital each contributed and the time for which it was available. If the total profit for the first year is £10 500, calculate the total amount each partner receives. [L]

Section 2
Mensuration

Units

In the metric system, the prefixes

milli (m) meaning $\frac{1}{1000}$th,

centi (c) meaning $\frac{1}{100}$th,

kilo (k) meaning 1000

are commonly used with a standard unit to form derived units.

Useful results and relationships are given below:

Length   1 km = 1000 m,   1 cm = $\frac{1}{100}$ m,   1 mm = $\frac{1}{1000}$ m

and, in particular,   1 m = 100 cm   and 1 cm = 10 mm.

Area   1 km² (1 square kilometre) = 1000 m × 1000 m = 10^6 m²,

1 m² (1 square metre) = 100 cm × 100 cm = 10^4 cm²,

1 cm² (1 square centimetre) = 10 mm × 10 mm = 100 mm².

The quantity 10 000 m² is known as a *hectare*.

Volume   1 km³ (1 cubic kilometre) = $(1000)^3$ m³ = 10^9 m³.

Similarly 1 m³ = $(100 \text{ cm})^3$ = 10^6 cm³ and

1 cm³ = $(10 \text{ mm})^3$ = 1000 mm³.

Capacity   1 litre (l) is the standard unit: 1 l = 1000 ml = 1000 cm³

Mass   1 kg = 1000 g, where g stands for *gram*.

1 tonne = 1000 kg = 10^6 g (megagram).

Note: In converting units of area or volume, or for finding areas and volumes of scaled figures

$$\text{area scale factor} = (\text{linear scale factor})^2,$$
$$\text{volume scale factor} = (\text{linear scale factor})^3.$$

Examples: (a) 1 m = 100 cm, 1 m² = $(100)^2$ cm² = 10^4 cm²,
1 m³ = 10^6 cm³.

(b) On a map whose scale factor is 1 : 50 000, the area of a lake is 32 cm².

The actual area of the lake = $(50\,000)^2 \times 32 \text{ cm}^2 = \dfrac{(50\,000)^2 \times 32}{(10^5)^2} \text{ km}^2$

$$= 8 \text{ km}^2.$$

(c) If the volume of a solid figure is 1120 cm³, the volume of a similar figure scaled down in the ratio 1 : 4 will be $\left(\dfrac{1}{4}\right)^3 \times 1120 \text{ cm}^3 = 17{\cdot}5 \text{ cm}^3$.

Important formulae for calculating lengths and areas of plane figures are:

Rectangle   : *Area = length × breadth.*

Triangle   : *Area = $\frac{1}{2}$ × base × height [$\frac{1}{2}ab$ sin C, see Section 9].*

Parallelogram   : *Area = base × height [$\frac{1}{2}$ × product of diagonals can be used for rhombus].*

Trapezium   : *Area = $\frac{1}{2}$ × (sum of parallel sides) × perpendicular distance between them.*

Circle   : *Circumference = 2πr, Area = πr².*

Sector of circle   : *Arc length (l) = $\dfrac{\theta}{360}$ × 2πr,*

$$Sector\ area\ (A) = \frac{\theta}{360} \times \pi r^2. \text{ [Figure 2.4.]}$$

π is an irrational number; the value $\frac{22}{7}$ is used if cancelling is possible, otherwise the decimal values 3·14 or 3·142 are used.
Figures 2.1, 2.2, 2.3, 2.4 illustrate the results.

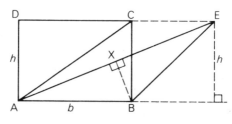

Fig. 2.1

Area $\triangle ABC = \frac{1}{2}$ × area of rectangle ABCD
$$= \tfrac{1}{2}bh$$
Area $\triangle ABE$ = area $\triangle ABC$ (a shear preserves area)
⇒ Area $\triangle ABE = \frac{1}{2}bh$
Note that area $\triangle ABE = \frac{1}{2}$ × AE × BX also.

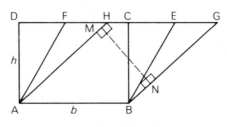

Fig. 2.2

Area parallelogram ABGH = area parallelogram ABEF
                             = area rectangle ABCD (shear)
                             = bh.
Note that area parallelogram ABGH = BG × MN also.

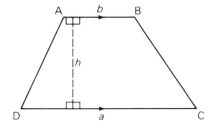

Fig. 2.3

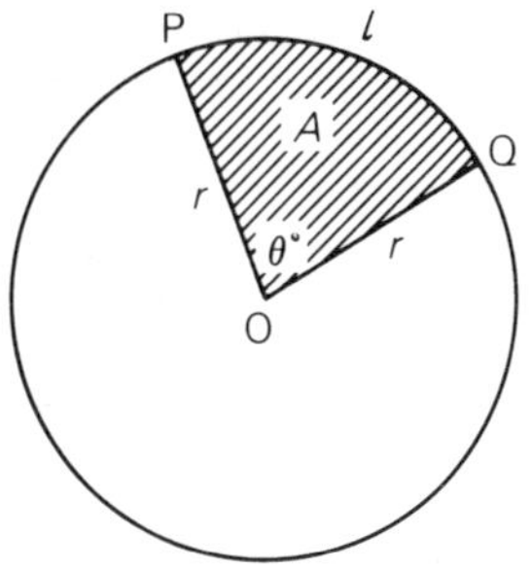

Fig. 2.4

For trapezium ABCD
Area $= \frac{1}{2}(a+b)h.$

$$l = \frac{\theta}{360} \times 2\pi r, \ A = \frac{\theta}{360} \times \pi r^2.$$

Example 1: *In Figure 2.1, if b = 4 cm, h = 5 cm and AE = 8 cm, calculate the length of BX, the perpendicular from B to AE.*

Area of $\triangle ABE = \frac{1}{2}bh = \frac{1}{2} \times 4 \times 5 \text{ cm}^2 = 10 \text{ cm}^2.$
But if AE is considered as the base of $\triangle ABE$, area $= \frac{1}{2} \times AE \times BX$

$$\Rightarrow \tfrac{1}{2} \times 8 \times BX = 10 \Rightarrow BX = 2\tfrac{1}{2} \text{ cm}.$$

Example 2: *In Figure 2.4, if θ = 30° and r = 14 cm, calculate the area of shaded sector POQ. Calculate the radius of the circle whose area is equal to that of sector POQ.*

$$\text{Sector area} = \frac{\cancel{30}^{\,1}}{\cancel{360}_{12_{\,6_3}}} \times \pi \times \cancel{14}^{\,7} \times \cancel{14}^{\,7} \text{ cm}^2 = \frac{49\pi}{3} \text{ cm}^2.$$

For second circle $\quad \pi r^2 = \dfrac{49\pi}{3} \Rightarrow r = 4.04 \text{ cm}$ (3 s.f.).

Formulae for calculating areas and volumes of solid figures are:

PRISM (a solid with constant cross-sectional area)

Volume = area of cross-section × perpendicular distance between ends.

Cuboid (cross-section is a rectangle)

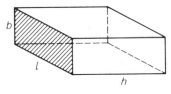

Fig. 2.5

$$V = b \times l \times h$$

Triangular prism

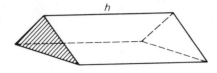

Fig. 2.6

$$V = \text{area of shaded triangle} \times h$$

Cylinder (cross-section is a circle)

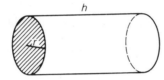

Fig. 2.7

$$V = \pi r^2 h$$

Curved surface area (CSA) $= 2\pi rh$
Total surface area (TSA) $= 2\pi rh + 2\pi r^2$ (closed)
$$= 2\pi r(h + r)$$

PYRAMID   Volume $= \frac{1}{3} \times$ (base area) $\times$ height

Rectangular Based   *Tetrahedron* (triangular based)

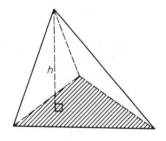

Fig. 2.8   *Fig. 2.9*

$V = \frac{1}{3} \times l \times b \times h$ $V = \frac{1}{3} \times \text{area of shaded triangle} \times h$

14

Cone (circular based)

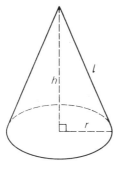

Fig. 2.10

Figure 2.10 shows a right circular cone (vertex directly above centre of base).

$$V = \tfrac{1}{3}\pi r^2 h \text{ for all circular cones.}$$

For a right circular cone

Curved surface area $= \pi r l$ (l is the slant edge)

Total surface area $= \pi r l + \pi r^2 = \pi r(l + r)$

SPHERE   Surface area $= 4\pi r^2$,   Volume $= \tfrac{4}{3}\pi r^3$.
(Note that all spheres are similar to each other.)

Example 1:   *A hollow spherical ball with internal and external diameters of 19 cm and 21 cm respectively is made of material of density 6·8 g/cm³. Calculate (i) the volume of material in the ball (ii) the mass of the material. (Take $\pi = 3·14$.)*

The internal and external *radii* are 9·5 cm and 10·5 cm.
(i) The required volume = volume of sphere of radius 10·5 cm

$\qquad\qquad\qquad\qquad$ – volume of sphere of radius 9·5 cm

$\qquad\qquad\qquad\quad = \tfrac{4}{3}\pi \,(10·5^3 - 9·5^3)$

$\qquad\qquad\qquad\quad = 1257 \text{ cm}^3.$

(ii) Mass of material $\quad = 1257 \times 6·8 \text{ g} = 8547·6 \text{ g} = 8·55 \text{ kg (3 s.f.).}$

Example 2:   *Figure 2.11 shows the cross-section of a child's toy consisting of a cone joined to a hemisphere. The height of the cone is 14 cm and their common radius is $10\tfrac{1}{2}$ cm. Calculate (i) the volume of the toy, (ii) its surface area. (Take $\pi = \tfrac{22}{7}$.)*

(i) Volume = volume of cone + volume of hemisphere

$\qquad = \tfrac{1}{3}\pi r^2 h + \tfrac{2}{3}\pi r^3 = \tfrac{1}{3}\pi r^2(h + 2r)$

$\qquad = \dfrac{1}{\cancel{3}} \times \dfrac{\cancel{22}^{11}}{\cancel{7}} \times \dfrac{\cancel{21}}{\cancel{2}_1} \times \dfrac{21}{2} \times 35 \text{ cm}^3$

$\qquad = 4042\tfrac{1}{2} \text{ cm}^3.$

15

(ii) Surface area $= \pi r l + 2\pi r^2$, where $l = \sqrt{(14^2 + (10\frac{1}{2})^2)} = 17\frac{1}{2}$ cm,
$$= \pi r(l + 2r)$$

$$= \frac{22^{11}}{7_1} \times \frac{21^3}{2_1} \times \frac{77}{2} = 1270\frac{1}{2} \text{ cm}^2.$$

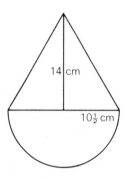

14 cm

$10\frac{1}{2}$ cm

Fig. 2.11

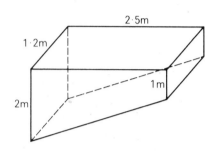

2·5m

1·2m

2m

1m

Fig. 2.12

Example 3: *A tank with dimensions shown in Figure 2.12 is to be filled with water through a pipe of cross sectional area 200 cm². If the speed of the water is 8 metres per minute, calculate the time taken to fill the tank.*

The tank is a prism with a trapezium as its cross-section.

$$\text{Area of trapezium} = \tfrac{1}{2}(1 + 2) \times 2\text{·}5 = 3\text{·}75 \text{ m}^2.$$
$$\text{Volume of tank} = 3\text{·}75 \times 1\text{·}2 \text{ m}^3 = 4\text{·}5 \text{ m}^3.$$

In 1 minute volume of water entering $= \dfrac{200}{(100)^2} \times 8 \text{ m}^3 = 0\text{·}16 \text{ m}^3.$

Time taken $= \dfrac{4\text{·}5}{0\text{·}16}$ minutes $= 28\frac{1}{8}$ minutes.

Exercise 2.1
(Take π to be $\frac{22}{7}$ unless otherwise instructed)

1 Square tiles of side 20 cm cost 15p each. Calculate (i) the cost, in £, of 500 tiles, (ii) the number of tiles required to cover a square ceiling of side 5 m. [C]
2 The price of a rectangular piece of material which is 6 metres long is £4·95. Calculate the width of the material if it costs £1·10 per square metre. [L]
3 A rectangular box with a square base is 18 cm high and has a volume of 882 cm³. Calculate the perimeter of the square base. [L]
4 On a map whose scale is 1:50 000, a forest is represented by an area of 6 cm². Find in square centimetres the area representing this forest on a map whose scale is 1:100 000. [C]
5 On a map with a scale of 1 : 200 000, towns P and Q are 5 cm apart. What is the actual distance, in km, between them?
   The same two towns are 2 cm apart on a map with a scale of 1:n. Find n. [M]

6 (a) Find the number of cubes of side 1 cm that can be fitted exactly into a box with internal dimensions 4 cm by 6 cm by 10 cm.
(b) Find the number of cubes of side 2 cm that can be fitted exactly into the same box. [CA]

7 On a map, drawn to a scale of 3 cm to 1 km, the area of a lake is 10·89 cm². Calculate the actual area of the lake in km². [L]

8 The length l of a rectangle is increased by 30 % and its breadth b is decreased by 40 %. Obtain an expression for the new area of the rectangle. Hence calculate the percentage decrease in the area of the rectangle. [L]

9 Obtain an expression for the area of the four walls of a room if the room is l metres long, d metres wide and h metres high. [L]

10 On a map drawn to a scale of 1 : 2500, calculate the actual area of a field in m² if the field is represented on the map by a rectangle measuring 2 cm by 1·2 cm. [L]

11 A rectangular field has a length of 105 m and an area of 0·84 hectare. Calculate the width of the field. The field is sown with grass seed at a rate of 15 grams per square metre. What is the total cost at £0·60 per kilogram? [O]

12 The volume of a closed rectangular box is 120 cm³ and the length of its base is twice its width. If the width of the box is x cm, express in terms of x, as simply as possible, (i) the height of the box, (ii) its total surface area. [C]

13 The circumference of a circle is 22 cm. Taking π to be $\frac{22}{7}$, calculate the radius and, hence, the area of this circle. [L]

14 Calculate the radius of a circle whose area is equal to the sum of the areas of four circles of radii 2 cm, 4 cm, 5 cm and 6 cm respectively. [JMB]

15 The height of a cylinder is three times the radius of the base. If the volume of the cylinder is 192π cm³, calculate the radius of the base. [L]

16 A cylindrical garden roller has a diameter of 40 cm and is 70 cm wide. Calculate the area, in m², rolled during 100 revolutions of the roller. [L]

17 A circular pond of diameter 3·22 m is surrounded by a path 28 cm wide. Calculate the area of the pond and the area of the path. Give your answers in m² correct to 2 decimal places. [L]

18 The curved surface area of a solid circular cylinder of height 7 cm is 110 cm². Calculate the volume of the same cylinder. [JMB]

19 The area of a sector of a circle of radius 6 cm is 33 cm². Using $\pi = \frac{22}{7}$, calculate the angle of the sector. [L]

20 A chord LM of a circle of radius 7 cm subtends an angle of 90° at the centre O. Calculate the areas of the two parts into which the chord LM divides the sector LOM. [L]

21 Calculate the number of *complete* revolutions made by a cycle wheel of diameter 70 cm in travelling a distance of $\frac{1}{2}$ km. [L]

22 A cylindrical tank has height 1 m and diameter 80 cm. Calculate its volume in litres correct to one significant figure. [O]

23 A closed rectangular box is made of wood 1 cm thick. Its external dimensions are 80 cm by 50 cm by 42 cm. Calculate (a) the inside volume of the box, (b) the total surface area of the outside of the box. [L]

24 A model of a minibus is made to a scale 1 : 20. The height of the model is 10 cm.
(a) What is the height in metres of the full-sized minibus?
(b) The volume of the model minibus is 2500 cm³. Calculate the area of the base of the full-sized minibus. [S]

25 A circular disc of radius 3 cm is cut out of a square sheet of metal of side 10 cm. Calculate correct to two significant figures (i) the area of the disc; (ii) the percentage of the metal sheet which was wasted. [O]

26 When a car is travelling at 66 km/h, the wheels are rotating at a rate of 625 revolutions per minute. Calculate the radius of a wheel, giving your answer in centimetres. [L]

27 Given that 1 cm³ of brass weighs 8·45 grams, calculate the weight of a solid

cylinder of brass whose radius is 1·3 cm and whose length is 9·0 cm.   [L]

28   The height of a cone is one-third that of an exactly similar cone. Given that the volume of the larger cone is 81 cm³, find the volume of the smaller cone.

[JMB]

Exercise 2.2

(Take π to be $\frac{22}{7}$ unless otherwise instructed)

1   (i) Find the area of a circle of diameter 5·6 cm, giving your answer in cm² correct to two significant figures.
(ii) A fence which surrounds a rectangular field of length 300 metres and breadth 184 metres is taken down and is just long enough to fence in a circular paddock. Calculate the radius of the paddock.   [L]

2   The length of one side of a building is 20 m, and the length of the corresponding side of a scale model of the building is 40 cm.
(a) Given that the height of the building is 34 m, calculate the height of the model.
(b) Given that the width of a particular door in the model is 1·6 cm, calculate the width of the corresponding door in the building.   [L]

3   (i) Re-arrange the formula $\frac{4}{3}\pi r^3 = V$ so as to express r as a function of V.
(ii) A solid metal rectangular block whose dimensions are 9 cm by 11 cm by 49 cm is melted down and recast as a solid sphere. Calculate the radius of this sphere.   [JMB]

4   A vessel is in the shape of a cone with vertex downwards, axis vertical and the top is a horizontal circle. Water is poured into it to a depth of 30 cm and the radius of the circular water surface is 22 cm. Calculate the volume of the water in the vessel.
    A metal sphere is placed in the water so that it is totally immersed and the water level rises by 3 cm. Show that the radius of the new water surface is 24·2 cm and calculate the radius of the sphere.
    (The volume of a cone of radius r cm and height h cm is $\frac{1}{3}\pi r^2 h$ cm³. The volume of a sphere of radius s cm is $\dfrac{4\pi s^3}{3}$ cm³. Take π to be 3·14.)   [AEB]

5   A photograph which measures 7 cm by 9 cm is enlarged so that the longer side of the enlargement is $22\frac{1}{2}$ cm. Calculate (a) the length of the smaller side of the enlargement, (b) the area of the enlargement.
    In the original photograph a particular section has an area of 2 cm². Calculate the area of the corresponding section in the enlargement.   [L]

6   A rectangular lawn is 14 m long and 10 m wide and is to be surrounded by a gravel path, 1 m wide. The gravel is to be 5 cm deep and costs £12 per cubic metre. Calculate (a) the area of the lawn, (b) the area of the path, (c) the cost of the gravel required for the path.   [L]

7   (a) The **total** surface area of a solid cube is 600 cm². Find (i) the area, in cm², of one surface of the cube (ii) the length, in cm, of a side of the cube (iii) the cube's volume, in cm³.
(b) If the circumference of a circle is 31·4 cm, find the length of its radius, taking π to be 3·14.   [M]

8   A model M is a scale model of a solid S. The scale factor for any length from M to the corresponding length of S is 2.5×10^4, which is expressed in standard form, $a \times 10^b$, where $1 \leqslant a < 10$ and b is an integer. Calculate, in standard form, (i) the scale factor for volume from M to S, (ii) the scale factor for length from S to M.   [L]

9   A man constructs a rectangular swimming-pool, 10 m long and 3 m wide, in his garden and surrounds it with a rectangular paved area 2 m wide. The depth of the pool varies uniformly from 1 m at the shallow end to 2 m at the deep end. Calculate the paved area and the volume of water needed to fill the pool.

The pool is filled at a uniform rate. In 5 hours the water is $\frac{1}{3}$ m deep at the shallow end. Find the total time taken to fill the pool. [L]

10 A cylinder has a circular cross-section of radius 8 cm and a height of 12 cm. The formula for the volume, V, of such a cylinder is $V = \pi r^2 h$. Taking π as 3·14, find (a) the volume of this cylinder, (b) a formula for the height h in terms of π, r, V.

Use your answer to part (b) above to find (c) the height of a cylinder of radius 10 cm and volume 1000 cm^3. [M]

11 A group of 66 boys on a camping holiday is to sleep in tents, each of which is in the form of a circular cylinder of height 2 m surmounted by a cone of height 1 m, the diameter of each being 5 m. The volume of air space required by a boy inside a tent is 3 m^3. Calculate (a) the maximum number of boys which can be accommodated in a tent, (b) the minimum number of tents necessary to accommodate all 66 boys. [L]

12 A closed rectangular tank of length 4 m and width 3 m contains water to a depth of 2·5 m. Calculate the volume of water in the tank.

This water is pumped into a second tank through a pipe of cross-sectional area 0·05 m^2 at a constant speed of 4 m/s. Calculate the time taken to empty the first tank.

The dimensions of the second tank are proportional to those of the first tank. Given that the length of the second tank is 6 m, find its width.

Find also the depth of water in the second tank. [C]

13 A solid stone statue is 4 metres high and weighs 3600 kg. A solid plaster model of the statue is 80 cm high and weighs 16 kg. Calculate

(i) the ratio of the weights of the statue and model, (ii) the ratio of the volumes of the statue and model, (iii) the ratio of the weights of equal volumes of stone and plaster. [L]

14 In an experiment, a small spherical drop of oil is allowed to fall on to the surface of water so that it produces a thin film of oil covering a large area.

The volume of a drop was found to be 12·5 mm^3. Calculate the number of such drops which would be produced by 5000 mm^3 of oil.

Given that the volume V of a sphere of radius r is $\frac{4}{3}\pi r^3$, express r in terms of V and π. Taking π to be 3·14, calculate the radius of one drop.

A single drop is found to produce a circular oil film of area 1100 cm^2. Calculate the thickness of the film in millimetres, expressing your answer in standard form. [C]

15 The length of a swimming-pool used for races is 40 m.

(a) One competitor in a race gave up after swimming 15 lengths. How far had he swum?

(b) A competitor in a 2 km race gave up after swimming 23 lengths. How many more lengths would he have had to swim to complete the race?

(c) Another competitor swims for 3 km at an average speed of 0·5 m/s. How many minutes does he take?

(d) In a relay race a team has three members and each member swims three lengths of the pool. The breaststroke section is swum at a speed of $2x$ m/s, the backstroke at $3x$ m/s and the crawl at $4x$ m/s. Find, in terms of x, the total time for the race.

(e) If in fact the total time for the relay race in (d) is 260 seconds form an equation in x and solve it to find the value of x. [S]

Section 3
Sets and binary operations

The make-up of sets and operations on sets are of basic importance to the whole of mathematics. A set is a collection of objects, symbols or just things having some common property. The members of a set are called *elements* and they need to have two conditions attached to them:

(i) it must be possible to say whether or not any element belongs to a set,

(ii) it must be possible to pick out each element in a set individually.

Examples of sets are

the set C of chapters in this book,

the set T of people who are members of a trade union in the UK,

the set $\mathbb{N}$ of natural numbers.

A set can be described either by listing all of its elements as we have done for the chapters in this book or by defining a general property which every member of the set has. The sets T and $\mathbb{N}$ are written inside curly brackets read as 'the set'

$$T = \{\text{trade union members in the UK}\},$$
$$\mathbb{N} = \{n : n \in \text{natural numbers}\};$$

this second one is read as 'the set of elements n, such that n is a member of the set of natural numbers'.

The number of elements in the set C, written $n(C)$ or $n\{C\}$, is 10: $n(T)$ is a large number but it could be found, whereas $n(\mathbb{N})$ is, of course, infinite.

The set M of people who belong to the union of miners in the UK are also members of T and we write $M \subset T$, read as 'the set M is a subset of T'. We may also write $T \supset M$, read as 'the set T contains the set M'.

Disjoint Sets

Two sets are said to be *disjoint* if they have no members in common. For example, the set of teachers in a school and a set of children in the school are disjoint because they have no members in common.

The empty set $\varnothing$

The set which contains no elements is called $\varnothing$.

Universal sets (denoted by $\mathscr{E}$)

In order to investigate relations between certain sets, it is often necessary to define a set, called *the universal set*. All the other sets under discussion are subsets of this universal set.

Equality of sets

Two sets are equal, if and only if, they have exactly the same elements as members of each.

Venn diagrams

These diagrams provide a simple way of illustrating sets, the individual members of each set being placed inside a closed figure, usually a circle. The universal set, if defined, should enclose all other sets and is often denoted by a rectangle.

Operations on sets

Complement

For a universal set $\mathscr{E}$ and a subset A, the complement A' of A consists of all elements in $\mathscr{E}$ which are not in A.

Union of two set $A \cup B$

The operation of union between two sets A and B forms a set written $A \cup B$ whose members belong to either A or B or both A and B.

Intersection of two sets $A \cap B$

The operation of intersection between two sets A and B forms a set written $A \cap B$ whose members belong to both A and B.

Figure 3.1 shows the various cases which may arise and a list of special results is given for each of these.

Example 1: *Given that*

$$\mathscr{E} = \{k : k \text{ is an integer such that } 1 \leqslant k \leqslant 12\},$$
$$A = \{x : x \text{ is an integer such that } 1 < x < 10\},$$
$$B = \{y : y \text{ is a multiple of 3 and } 3 \leqslant y \leqslant 12\},$$

draw a Venn diagram to display this information and find the number of elements in the sets $A \cup B$, $A \cap B$, A', $A' \cap B'$.

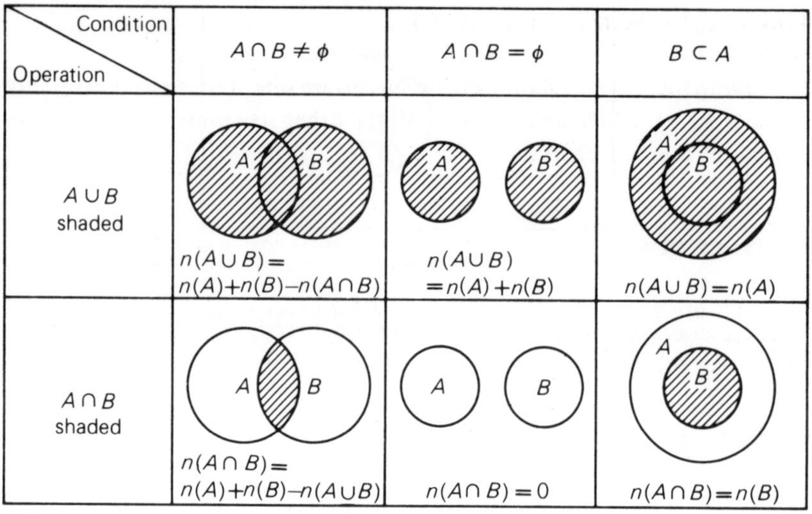

Operation \ Condition	$A \cap B \neq \phi$	$A \cap B = \phi$	$B \subset A$
$A \cup B$ shaded	$n(A \cup B) =$ $n(A)+n(B)-n(A \cap B)$	$n(A \cup B)$ $= n(A) + n(B)$	$n(A \cup B) = n(A)$
$A \cap B$ shaded	$n(A \cap B) =$ $n(A)+n(B)-n(A \cup B)$	$n(A \cap B) = 0$	$n(A \cap B) = n(B)$

Fig. 3.1   Operations on sets A and B

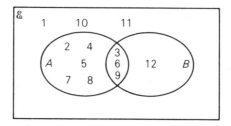

Fig. 3.2

By using the Venn diagram shown in Figure 3.2, the following results are obtained by counting the elements in each of the required sets: $n(A \cup B) = 9$, $n(A \cap B) = 3$, $n(A') = 4$, $n(A' \cap B') = 3$.

Example 2:   *The following survey was undertaken about the 30 children in a class: B is the set of children who have a bicycle and D is the set of children who have a dog; $n(B) = 23$, $n(D) = 10$ and $n(B \cap D) = 6$.*
Find (a) the number of children who have both a bicycle and a dog,
(b) the number of children who have neither a bicycle nor a dog,
(c) the number of children who have either a bicycle or a dog, but not both.

Draw the Venn diagram as marked in Figure 3.3 and place 6 in the region representing the set $B \cap D$. Since there are 23 children altogether in B there will be 17 in the region representing B only. In the same way, there will be 4 in the region representing D only and because there are 30 in the class there will be 3 left to place in the region representing those who have neither a bicycle nor a dog.

22

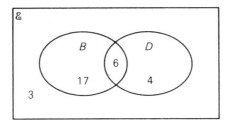

Fig. 3.3

The answers required can now be obtained directly from the diagram and are (a) 6, (b) 3, (c) 21.

Binary operations

Many sets which are met in mathematics have rules laid down in order to combine the elements in a set. Addition, subtraction, multiplication and division are four rules used for combining elements from sets of numbers like the positive integers, the rational numbers and the real numbers, except, of course, division by zero is not allowed. In sets we have met the operations of union and intersection. Such rules of combination are called **binary operations**. Let us suppose that we have a set A and a rule for combining ordered pairs of the elements of the set A. If the rule of combination produces for each pair an element which also belongs to A, then the rule is called a **binary operation** on the set A.

The associative property

Definition A binary operation $*$ on the set A is associative if and only if, for all elements $a, b, c, \ldots \in A$,

$$a * (b * c) = (a * b) * c.$$

The commutative property

Definition A binary operation $*$ on the set A is commutative if and only if, for all elements $a, b, \ldots \in A$,

$$a * b = b * a.$$

The distributive property

The binary operation ∇ is distributive over the binary operation $*$ if and only if, for all elements $a, b, c, \ldots \in A$,

$$a \nabla (b * c) = (a \nabla b) * (a \nabla c).$$

Under addition any real number remains unchanged when zero is added and under multiplication any real number remains unchanged when multiplied by 1.

23

Identity element

Definition An element e of a set A is called an identity element for the binary operation $*$ if and only if

$$a * e = e * a = a,$$

for every element $a \ldots \in A$.

Inverse elements

If $a, a' \in A$, whose identity element under the binary operation $*$ is e, and $a * a' = a' * a = e$, then a' is called the inverse of a under $*$ for the set A.

Example 1: For the set of real numbers under the operation multiplication, the identity element is 1 and since $2 \times \frac{1}{2} = \frac{1}{2} \times 2 = 1, \frac{1}{2}$ is the inverse of 2 under this operation.

Example 2: For $\{0, 1, 2, 3, 4\}$, form an operation table under the binary operation addition modulo 5, denoted by $*$. [Here $a * b$ is the remainder when $a + b$ is divided by 5.]

Second element

$*$	0	1	2	3	4
0	0	1	2	3	4
1	1	2	3	4	0
2	2	3	4	0	1
3	3	4	0	1	2
4	4	0	1	2	3

First element

Exercise 3.1

1 P and Q are two sets. $n(P) = 17$ and $n(Q) = 5$. If $Q \subset P$, write down the value of   (i) $n(P \cup Q)$,   (ii) $n(P \cap Q')$.   [CA]

2 $\mathscr{E} = \{1, 2, 3, 4, 5, 6, 7, 8, 9, 10\}, A = \{1, 2, 5, 10\}$ and $B = \{1, 4, 6, 8, 9, 10\}$. List the elements of   (i) $A \cap B$,   (ii) B'.   [CA]

3 The universal set $\{2, 3, 4, 5, 6, 7, 8\}$ has subsets $A = \{2, 4, 8\}$ and $B = \{2, 4, 6\}$. List the members of   (i) $A \cap B$,   (ii) $(A' \cup B') \cup (A \cap B)$.   [JMB]

4 If $\mathscr{E} = \{\text{living creatures}\}$, $M = \{\text{mammals}\}$, $C = \{\text{cats}\}$, $W = \{\text{water-creatures}\}$, write the following statements in symbolic form:
   (i) some mammals are water-creatures,
   (ii) no cats are water-creatures,
   (iii) all cats are mammals.
   Draw a single Venn diagram to illustrate these three statements.   [L]

5 The set $A = \{1, 2, 4, 8\}$. Write down the four subsets of A, each of which contains three elements. If one of these subsets is chosen at random, find the probability
   (i) that the mean of the elements of the subset is more than 3,
   (ii) that the median element of the subset is more than 3.   [L]

6 If $\mathscr{E}$ = {numbers with 2 digits},
   A = {even numbers with 2 digits},
   B = {multiples of 3 with 2 digits},
   C = {multiples of 4 with 2 digits},
   draw a Venn diagram to illustrate the relations between $\mathscr{E}$, A, B and C.
       State which of the following sets is empty; for each non-empty set describe
   the set in words as concisely as possible, and give one member of it:
   (a) $B \cap C$, (b) $A' \cap C$, (c) $A \cup C$.   [L]
7 (a) If R = {rhombuses} and P = {parallelograms}, simplify $R \cap P$.
   (b) The sets C and D are such that $n(C \cup D) = 44$, $n(C \cap D) = 11$ and
   $n(C) = 31$. Find the value of $n(D)$.   [C]
8 $\mathscr{E}$ = {4, 5, 6, 7, 8, 9, 10, 11, 12}.
   List the members of each of the following sets;
   (i) {multiples of 3},
   (ii) {factors of 385},
   (iii) $\{x : 24 - 3x = 9\}$,
   (iv) $\{y : 3y > 25\}$,
   (v) $\{z : (z - 6)^2 = 4\}$.   [AEB]
9 Under the operation of multiplication, compile tables for the sets $\{-1, 1\}$
   and $\{-1, 0, 1\}$. Name the identity elements and any inverse elements.   [L]
10 In the Universal set $\mathscr{E}$ = {natural numbers $n : 20 \leqslant n \leqslant 30$},
                          A = {multiples of 2},
                          B = {multiples of 3},
                          P = {prime numbers}.
   Draw a Venn diagram showing $\mathscr{E}$, A, B and P, indicating that part of your
   diagram which contains the number 25.   [L]
11 A, B and C are subsets of the universal set $\mathscr{E}$; $A \cap B = \varnothing$ and C is a subset of B.
   Draw a Venn diagram to show the relationship between $\mathscr{E}$, A, B, C. [JMB]
12 List all the subsets of the set $\{a, b, c\}$.   [JMB]

Exercise 3.2

1 In a certain class, the 26 pupils all take one or more of the three subjects
   Mathematics, Physics and Chemistry. 5 pupils study all three subjects, 6 study
   Mathematics and Physics only, 2 study Mathematics and Chemistry only and 4
   study Physics and Chemistry only. The number of pupils who study one subject
   only is divided equally between Mathematics, Physics and Chemistry.
       Illustrate the above information by a labelled Venn diagram, showing clearly
   the number in each separate region. Hence find the *total* number of pupils who
   are studying Mathematics.   [C]
2 For the purposes of this question, the following statements are assumed true:
                A : All politicians are optimists.
                B : Some optimists are idealists.
   (i) (a) Given that $\mathscr{E}$ = {people}, P = {politicians} and O = {optimists}, draw
   a Venn diagram for $\mathscr{E}$, P and O and write statement A in symbolic form, using
   any of the symbols

$$\cap, \ \cup, \ \subset, \ ', \ \mathscr{E}, \ \varnothing, \ =, \ \neq.$$

   (b) Similarly, draw a second Venn diagram for $\mathscr{E}$, O and I, where
   I = {idealists}. Write statement B in symbolic form.
   (c) Indicate why $P \cap I \neq \varnothing$ is not necessarily true.
   (ii) (a) The statements A and B are applied to a group of 15 people (i.e.
   $n(\mathscr{E}) = 15$). Given that $n(O) = 10$ and $n(I) = 8$, find the set of possible values of
   $n(O \cap I)$.
   (b) Given further that $n(P) = 6$, find the set of possible values of $n(P \cap I)$.
                                                                                       [L]

3 In this question

$\mathscr{E} = \{\text{quadrilaterals}\}$,
$A = \{\text{quadrilaterals with all four sides equal}\}$,
$B = \{\text{quadrilaterals with at least three sides equal}\}$,
$C = \{\text{quadrilaterals with no axes of symmetry}\}$.

Marking any equal sides and showing any axes of symmetry, sketch a member of each of the following sets:

(i) $A \cap C'$, (ii) $B \cap A' \cap C$, (iii) $B \cap A' \cap C'$, (iv) $C' \cap B'$.

Express in symbolic form the following statements:

(a) There are no quadrilaterals with all four sides equal but no axes of symmetry.

(b) There are some quadrilaterals with three sides equal and no axes of symmetry.

Draw a Venn diagram to illustrate the relation between $\mathscr{E}$, A, B and C.

[L]

4 (i) On the same diagram on graph paper, illustrate carefully the locus of a point $P(x, y)$ moving in a plane in each of the following (different) cases.

$R = \{(x, y) : 2 \leqslant x + y \leqslant 6\}$,
$S = \{P : \text{the angle APB} \geqslant 90°, \text{where A is the point } (2, 0) \text{ and B is the point } (6, 0)\}$.

(ii) Shade the region of the plane defined by $R \cap S$ and list the set of points $Q(x, y)$, $Q \subset R \cap S$, such that x and y are both integers. Find the distance between members of Q which are furthest apart. [AEB]

5 (a) The operation $\oplus$ is defined on the set $\{0, 1, 2, 3\}$ by $p \oplus q =$ the remainder when $p + q$ is divided by 4. Construct an operation table showing the values of $p \oplus q$ for all the pairs of elements from the set.

Use your table to obtain (i) the identity element, (ii) the inverse of 2, (iii) the solutions of $x \oplus (x \oplus x) = x$.

(b) The operation $\otimes$ is defined on the set $\{1, 3, 7, 9\}$ by $r \otimes s =$ the remainder when rs is divided by 10. Construct a table to illustrate this operation.

Use your table to obtain (i) the identity element, (ii) the inverse of 9.

(c) Write down a correspondence between the elements of the two sets to illustrate the fact that the operation $\oplus$ on the set $\{0, 1, 2, 3\}$ is isomorphic to the operation $\otimes$ on the set $\{1, 3, 7, 9\}$. [JMB]

6 The operation $*$ on two numbers means:

'Add the numbers together and divide by 2, ignoring any remainder' so that, for example,

$$6*8 = 7, \quad 6*7 = 6.$$

Write down the values of (a) $3*9$, (b) $4*7$.

Find a set of values for each of x, y and z if

(c) $3*x = 5$, (d) $y*y = 5$, (e) $3*z = z$.

Draw up the operation table for the set $\{1, 2, 3, 4\}$ under the operation $*$.

Explain what is meant by saying that the set is closed under the operation.

Explain how you can tell that neither an identity element nor inverse elements exist for this set under this operation.

State the condition under which a set of integers is closed under $*$. [L]

Section 4
Basic algebraic manipulation

Example 1: *Given that $a = 2$, $b = -3$ and $c = -5$, evaluate*
(i) $b^2 - 4ac$, (ii) $(a + b)(b - 2c)$.

(i) $b^2 - 4ac = (-3)^2 - 4(2)(-5) = 9 + 40 = 49$.
(ii) $a + b = 2 + (-3) = -1$,
$b - 2c = -3 - 2(-5) = -3 + 10 = 7$,
$(a + b)(b - 2c) = (-1)(7) = -7$.

Example 2: *A boy borrows £m from his father in order to buy a bicycle. The boy agrees to pay back £n each week from the money he earns delivering newspapers.*
(a) *Write down an expression for the amount still owing after w weeks.*
(b) *Given that the debt is exactly repaid after a further 4 weeks, find w in terms of m and n.*

(a) After w weeks the boy has repaid £wn.
$$\text{Amount still owing } £(m - wn).$$
(b) In 4 weeks the boy pays back £$4n$.
Therefore
$$m - wn = 4n$$
$$\Leftrightarrow m - 4n = wn$$
$$\Leftrightarrow w = \frac{m - 4n}{n}.$$

Example 3: *Given that $T = 2\pi \sqrt{\left(\dfrac{h^2 + k^2}{gh}\right)}$,*
(a) *find, to one decimal place, the value of T when $\pi = 3{\cdot}14$, $g = 10$, $h = 6{\cdot}4$ and $k = 4{\cdot}8$,*
(b) *express k in terms of the other symbols.*

(a) $T = 2 \times 3{\cdot}14 \sqrt{\left(\dfrac{6{\cdot}4^2 + 4{\cdot}8^2}{10 \times 6{\cdot}4}\right)} = 6{\cdot}28$. Hence $T = 6{\cdot}3$ (1 d.p.).

(b) $T^2 = \dfrac{4\pi^2(h^2 + k^2)}{gh}$
$$\Leftrightarrow ghT^2 = 4\pi^2 h^2 + 4\pi^2 k^2$$
$$\Leftrightarrow 4\pi^2 k^2 = ghT^2 - 4\pi^2 h^2$$
$$\Leftrightarrow k^2 = \frac{ghT^2 - 4\pi^2 h^2}{4\pi^2}$$
$$\Leftrightarrow k = \pm\frac{1}{2\pi}\sqrt{(ghT^2 - 4\pi^2 h^2)}.$$

Example 4: *Express* $\dfrac{4a-b}{3} + \dfrac{a+3b}{9}$ *as a single fraction in its lowest terms.*

The lowest common denominator is 9.

$$\frac{4a-b}{3} + \frac{a+3b}{9} = \frac{3(4a-b)}{9} + \frac{a+3b}{9}$$

$$= \frac{12a - 3b + a + 3b}{9}$$

$$= \frac{13a}{9}.$$

Example 5: *Express* $\dfrac{1}{3x} + \dfrac{1}{2x} - \dfrac{1}{6x}$ *as a single fraction in its lowest terms.*

The lowest common denominator is $6x$.

$$\frac{1}{3x} + \frac{1}{2x} - \frac{1}{6x} = \frac{2}{6x} + \frac{3}{6x} - \frac{1}{6x} = \frac{4}{6x} = \frac{2}{3x}.$$

Note that, in this last example, the final answer can be further reduced after the single fraction has been found, since $\dfrac{4}{6x} = \dfrac{2}{3x}$.

Factors

$ab - ac = a(b-c)$. The factor a is called a **common factor**.
$a^2 - b^2 = (a-b)(a+b)$, the difference of two squares.

Example 1: *Factorise* (a) $x^2 - 4$, (b) $x^2 - 4x$, (c) $x^3 - 4x$.

(a) $x^2 - 4 = (x-2)(x+2)$ (the difference of two squares).
(b) $x^2 - 4x = x(x-4)$ (the factor x is common).
(c) $x^3 - 4x = x(x^2 - 4)$ (x is a common factor)
         $= x(x-2)(x+2)$ ($x^2 - 4$ can be factorised as before).

Factors of trinomials

Expressions of the type $ax^2 + bx + c$ are called **trinomials**.
The product of two linear factors forms a trinomial.

Example 2: $(x+3)(x-5) = x(x-5) + 3(x-5)$
                  $= x^2 - 5x + 3x - 15$
                  $= x^2 - 2x - 15.$

This method is reversible and can be used to split trinomials into their constituent factors, when such factors exist.
    For $x^2 - 2x - 15$, the coefficients of the x^2, x and constant terms are 1,

-2, and -15 respectively. Two numbers are required which have a product of $(1) \times (-15) = -15$ and which have a sum of -2.
The required numbers are -5 and 3 and the expression is rewritten as

$$x^2 - 5x + 3x - 15 = x(x-5) + 3(x-5)$$
$$= (x-5)(x+3).$$

Example 3: *Factorise* (a) $x^2 + 7x + 10$, (b) $3x^2 + 2x - 8$.

(a) Two numbers are required which have a product of 10 and a sum of 7. These are 5 and 2.

$$x^2 + 7x + 10 = x^2 + 5x + 2x + 10$$
$$= x(x+5) + 2(x+5)$$
$$= (x+5)(x+2).$$

(b) Two numbers are required having a product of -24 and a sum 2. These are 6 and -4.

$$3x^2 + 2x - 8 = 3x^2 + 6x - 4x - 8$$
$$= 3x(x+2) - 4(x+2)$$
$$= (x+2)(3x-4).$$

The factor theorem

From the previous example we know that $3x^2 + 2x - 8$ has factors $(x+2)$ and $(3x-4)$.
It is clear that $3x^2 + 2x - 8$ is 0 when $x = -2$ or when $x = \frac{4}{3}$.
Conversely, if an expression in x is zero for $x = a$, then $(x-a)$ is a factor of the expression. This result is called **the factor theorem**.

Example 4: *Given that the expression* $x^2 + kx + 12$ *has a factor* $(x+3)$, *find k.*

Since $(x+3)$ is a factor, the expression is 0 when $x = -3$.
$(-3)^2 + k(-3) + 12 = 0$ and hence $9 + 12 = 3k$ and $k = 7$.

Equations

Example 1: *Solve the equation* $\dfrac{x+1}{3} - \dfrac{3x-5}{4} = 4\frac{1}{2}$.

Multiply by 12, the lowest common denominator,

$$\Rightarrow 4(x+1) - 3(3x-5) = 54$$
$$\Leftrightarrow 4x + 4 - 9x + 15 = 54$$
$$\Leftrightarrow -35 = 5x$$
$$\Leftrightarrow x = -7.$$

Example 2: *Solve the equations (a) $x^2 - 14x + 45 = 0$,*
(b) $2x^2 - 5x - 12 = 0$.

(a) Factorising $(x - 5)(x - 9) = 0$.
Either $x - 5 = 0$ or $x - 9 = 0$. Therefore $x = 5$ or 9.
(b) Factorising $(2x + 3)(x - 4) = 0$.
Either $2x + 3 = 0$ or $x - 4 = 0$. Therefore $x = -\frac{3}{2}$ or 4.

Example 3: *Solve the equation $2x^2 - 8x - 7 = 0$, giving answers to 2 decimal places.*

Method 1 *Using completion of the square*

Divide by 2 and rearrange,
$$x^2 - 4x = 3 \cdot 5$$
$$\Leftrightarrow x^2 - 4x + 4 = 7 \cdot 5$$
$$\Leftrightarrow (x - 2)^2 = 7 \cdot 5$$
$$\Leftrightarrow x - 2 = \pm \sqrt{7 \cdot 5} = \pm 2 \cdot 739.$$

Either
$$x = 4 \cdot 739 \text{ or } x = -0 \cdot 739$$
$$\Rightarrow x = 4 \cdot 74 \text{ or } x = -0 \cdot 74 \quad \text{(2 decimal places)}.$$

Method 2 *Using the formula*

For the equation $ax^2 + bx + c = 0$, $\quad x = \dfrac{-b \pm \sqrt{(b^2 - 4ac)}}{2a}$.

In our equation, $a = 2$, $b = -8$ and $c = -7$.

Hence $\quad x = \dfrac{-(-8) \pm \sqrt{[(-8)^2 - 4(2)(-7)]}}{2 \times 2} = \dfrac{8 \pm \sqrt{(64 + 56)}}{4}$

$$\Rightarrow x = \frac{8 \pm \sqrt{120}}{4} = \frac{8 \pm 10 \cdot 95}{4}$$

$$\Rightarrow x = \frac{18 \cdot 95}{4} \quad \text{OR} \quad \frac{-2 \cdot 95}{4}$$

$$= 4 \cdot 74 \text{ or } -0 \cdot 74 \quad \text{(2 decimal places)}.$$

Note: In examination questions, you can usually tell when one of the above methods is required because the solutions will be required to a stated degree of accuracy. If no degree of accuracy is required, you should always try to factorise the quadratic equation first, and only resort to one of the above methods when the factors cannot be found easily.

Linear simultaneous equations

Example 4: *Solve for x and y the equations*

$$4x + 3y = 11 \ldots \text{(i)}$$
$$3x - 2y = 21 \ldots \text{(ii)}$$

Multiply (i) by 2 and (ii) by 3.

$$\Rightarrow 8x + 6y = 22,$$
$$9x - 6y = 63.$$

Adding
$$17x = 85 \Leftrightarrow x = \frac{85}{17} = 5.$$

Substituting $x = 5$ in (i) we get $20 + 3y = 11$
$$\Leftrightarrow 3y = 11 - 20 = -9$$
$$\Leftrightarrow y = -3.$$

Complete answer $x = 5$, $y = -3$.

Checking this solution in equation (ii) gives
      left hand side $= 3x - 2y = 15 + 6 = 21 =$ right hand side.

Example 5: *Solve for y the simultaneous equations*

$$2x - 3y = 1, \qquad \text{(i)}$$
$$3x + 7y = -56 \qquad \text{(ii)}$$

From (i) $2x = 3y + 1$ and hence $x = \frac{1}{2}(3y + 1)$.
Substituting in (ii) $\frac{3}{2}(3y + 1) + 7y = -56$.
Multiplying by 2, $3(3y + 1) + 14y = -112$.
Rearranging $\qquad\qquad 9y + 14y = -112 - 3$
$$\Leftrightarrow 23y = -115 \text{ and } y = -5.$$

This example could have been solved by the method used in the previous example as follows.
Multiply (i) by 3 and (ii) by 2

$$\Rightarrow 6x - 9y = 3,$$
$$6x + 14y = -112.$$

Subtracting the second from the first

$$-23y = 115$$
$$\Leftrightarrow y = -5.$$

The first method used here should be mastered because it has important applications when solving simultaneous equations with more unknowns or of higher degrees or both.

Example 6: *Find the set of values of x for which*

$$x^2 - 4x \geqslant 12.$$

$x^2 - 4x - 12 \equiv (x - 6)(x + 2)$
For $x \leqslant -2$, $x^2 - 4x - 12$ is $(-)(-)$ which is positive,
For $-2 \leqslant x \leqslant 6$, $x^2 - 4x - 12$ is $(-)(+)$ which is negative,
For $x \geqslant 6$, $x^2 - 4x - 12$ is $(+)(+)$ which is positive.
Hence $x^2 - 4x \geqslant 12$, when $x \leqslant -2$ and when $x \geqslant 6$.

Example 7: *Given that $p * q = p^q$, evaluate*
(*a*) $2 * 3$, (*b*) $3 * 2$, (*c*) $(2 * 3) * 2$, (*d*) $2 * (3 * 2)$.

(*a*) $2 * 3 = 2^3 = 8$.

31

(b) $3 * 2 = 3^2 = 9.$

(c) $(2 * 3) * 2 = 8 * 2 = 8^2 = 64.$

(d) $2 * (3 * 2) = 2 * 9 = 2^9 = 512.$

Exercise 4.1

1 Given that $a = 2$, $b = -3$ and $c = -4$, evaluate

    (a) $b^2 + c^2$,   (b) $b(c - a)$,   (c) $\dfrac{a - b}{b - c}$.

2 A rectangular sheet of stamps, worth 10 p each, has r rows containing n stamps each. Write down the total value of the sheet (a) in pence, (b) in £. Given that the total value of the sheet is £8, express r in terms of n.

3 Convert a speed of v cm/s into km/h.

4 Given that $y = bx^2 - c$, copy and complete the following table

x	b	c	y
2	3	4	
-5		16	34
$0 \cdot 5$	3		$2 \cdot 3$

5 Given that $p = kq^2 - qr$, express k in terms of p, q and r.

6 Find, in pence, the total profit when n plants costing c pence for 10 are sold at s pence each.

7 Given that $2ac = ab - bc$, express c in terms of a and b.

8 Express as a single fraction $\dfrac{1}{x} - \dfrac{1}{x - 2y}$.

9 Simplify $3x^2(x - y) - xy(2x - 3y)$.

10 Express $\dfrac{6x}{5} - \dfrac{4x + 3y}{3}$ as a single fraction.

11 Simplify $p^3q^2 \div p^2q^3$.

12 A man walks at an average speed of u km/h for t hours. He then travels by bus moving at an average speed of $10u$ km/h for $\frac{1}{4}t$ hours. Given that the total distance covered by the man is d km, express d in terms of u and t. If $t = 3$ and $d = 28$ find the average speed of the bus.

13 If $2 \leqslant a \leqslant 4$ and $3 \leqslant b \leqslant 6$, find

    (a) the greatest value of $a^2 - b^2$, (b) the least value of $\dfrac{a}{b}$.

14 Given that $T = 2\pi\sqrt{\dfrac{a}{g}}$, express g in terms of the other symbols. Find, to one decimal place, the value of a when $T = 2$, $\pi = 3 \cdot 14$ and $g = 9 \cdot 8$.

15 Solve the equation $\dfrac{x - 2}{3} = \dfrac{2x - 3}{7}$.

In questions **16–25** factorise each expression.

16 $x^2 - 49$ **17** $x^2 + 5x + 6$ **18** $x^2 - 7x - 18$

19 $4x^2 - 25$ **20** $x^2 - 8x + 12$ **21** $x^2 + 3x - 18$

22 $6x^2 - 17x + 5$ **23** $2x^2 - 32$ **24** $2x^2 + 7x - 4$

25 $10x^2 - 13x - 14.$

In questions **26–35** solve the equations.

26 $\dfrac{x + 1}{4} - \dfrac{2x - 1}{10} = \dfrac{1}{2}$ **27** $\dfrac{3x + 7}{3} + \dfrac{1 - 2x}{5} = \dfrac{4}{3}$

28 $4x^2 = 81$ **29** $x^2 - 9x + 20 = 0$ **30** $x^2 - 2x - 35 = 0$

31 $x^2 + 12x + 32 = 0$ **32** $x^2 + 4x - 77 = 0$ **33** $6x^2 - x - 2 = 0$

34 $2x^2 - 17x + 21 = 0$ **35** $10x^2 + 19x + 6 = 0.$

In questions **36–40** solve the equations giving your answers to two decimal places.

36 $x^2 - 6x + 7 = 0$ **37** $x^2 + 9x - 2 = 0$ **38** $2x^2 - 3x - 4 = 0$

39 $5x^2 - 8x + 2 = 0$ **40** $(2x + 1)(x + 2) = (x + 1)(x + 3)$.

In questions **41–45** find the solution set of each inequality.

41 $3(x - 2) \leqslant 2(7 - x)$ **42** $\dfrac{x}{2} > \dfrac{1 - x}{3}$ **43** $x^2 \geqslant 100$

44 $x^2 + 3x - 40 < 0$ **45** $\dfrac{x - 1}{x - 3} \geqslant 0.$

46 If $a * b = a - 2b$, find the values of (a) $3 * 2$,   (b) $2 * 3$,   (c) $(2 * 2) * 2$.

47 If $p * q = p + q^2$, find the values of (a) $(3 * 3) * 3$,   (b) $3 * (3 * 3)$.

In questions **48–52** solve the simultaneous equations for x and y.

48 $2x + 3y = 1,$ **49** $3x + 2y = 2,$ **50** $8x - y = 17,$
     $4x - y = 9.$ $x + y = 2.$ $6x - 4y = 29.$

51 $x = 2y + 1,$ **52** $5x - 4y = 17,$
     $6x + y = 45.$ $2x - 3y = 18.$

In questions **53–55**, express c in terms of a and b.

53 $b(a + c) = c(a - b)$ **54** $a = \dfrac{b + c}{b - c}$ **55** $\dfrac{2}{b} = 1 + \dfrac{a}{c}.$

Exercise 4.2

1   Find the value of $x(x + y)$ when $x = -2$ and $y = 1$.   [L]

2   If $p = 3$ and $q = -2$, calculate the value of $p^3 + q^3 - 3pq^2$.   [L]

3   If $a = 1$, $b = 2$ and $c = -3$, find the value of $\dfrac{c - ab}{c + ab}$.   [L]

4   Find the value of $3x^3 y^2$ when $x = -1$ and $y = 4$.   [C]

5   Solve the equations
    (i) $2y + 3 = 6 - 2y$,
    (ii) $t^2 + 4t = 0$.   [C]

6   Find the solution set for the inequality

$$x - \frac{x - 1}{3} < 1.$$

    Represent your solution set on the number line.   [L]

7   (i) Solve the equation $5x = 7 \cdot 5$.
    (ii) Simplify $3(y + 2) - (y - 1)$.
    (iii) Given that $v^2 = u^2 + 2fs$ and $u = 4$, $f = 5$ and $s = 2$, find the values of v.
                                                           [L]

8   Solve the equation $\dfrac{3x - 2}{5} - \dfrac{2x - 3}{4} = \dfrac{1}{2}.$ [L]

9   Solve the equation $\dfrac{x + 5}{3} - \dfrac{2x - 1}{4} = 2.$ [L]

10   Simplify

$$\frac{1}{(x + 1)(x + 2)} + \frac{1}{x + 2}.$$

                                                        [JMB]

11   Simplify the expression

$$\frac{7}{(x - 4)(x + 3)} - \frac{4}{(x + 3)(x - 1)}$$

    giving your answer as a single fraction in its lowest terms.   [C]

12   (i) Express as a single fraction in its lowest terms

$$\frac{4}{(x - 2)(x + 2)} - \frac{2}{x(x - 2)}.$$

(ii) A formula for the *sum* of the first n terms of a series is $\frac{1}{2}n(3n-1)$. Calculate the numerical value of the third term. [L]

13　(i) Simplify $(2a-b)(3a+2b)-b(a-2b)$.

　　(ii) Solve the equation $\dfrac{3x}{5}-\dfrac{x-3}{2}=\dfrac{x}{7}$. [L]

14　Solve the simultaneous equations
$$3x+5y=6,$$
$$6x-2y=48.$$
[C]

15　(i) Solve the equations
$$3x+4y=2,\qquad 4x-3y=11.$$

　　(ii) If $x=\dfrac{z}{5}+1$ and $y=\dfrac{z}{2}-1$, find the value of $5x-4y-1$ in terms of z.
[L]

16　(a) Given that y is directly proportional to x and that $y=2$ when $x=3$, find the value of y when $x=1$.

　　(b) Solve the simultaneous equations
$$3p-q=13,\qquad 2p+q=7.$$
[C]

17　Factorise completely (a) x^3-5x^2-14x,　(b) $ab-2b-3ac+6c$. [L]

18　Factorise completely (a) $5h^2-20k^2$,　(b) $(x-y)^2-3x+3y$. [L]

19　(i) Factorise $x^2+2xy+y^2$.

　　(ii) Given that $x^2+y^2=13$ and $xy=3$, calculate the value of $(x+y)^2$. [C]

20　(i) Factorise completely
　　　　(a) $2p^2-18q^2$,　(b) $(r+s)^2+r+s$.

　　(ii) Solve the equation $3x^2-7x+3=0$, giving your answers correct to two decimal places. [L]

21　(a) Factorise completely (i) b^2-4b,　(ii) c^2-9.

　　(b) Given that $x=\dfrac{2+y}{y}$, express y in terms of x.

　　(c) (i) Factorise $4n^2+29n+7$.

　　　(ii) Using your result for (c)(i), or otherwise, express 42 907 as the product of two whole numbers neither of which is 1. [AEB]

22　Solve $(4x-3)(x+2)(x-1)=0$, where x is a member of the set of
　(i) real numbers,　　(ii) natural numbers. [JMB]

23　Factorise (i) $10x^2-27x+11$,　　(ii) $4x^2-9y^2$. [JMB]

24　If $x-2$ is a factor of $3x^2-x-a$, find the value of a and find the other factor.
[L]

25　Solve the inequality
$$3(1-x)<2(2-x).$$
[L]

26　Solve each of these equations
　(a) $2(x-3)=6$,
　(b) $x^2-11x+18=0$. [M]

27　(a) Given that $x=2m-n$ and $y=m-2n$, express, in terms of m and n,
　(i) $x+y$, (ii) $x-y$.
　Given also that $x+y=3$ and $x-y=4$, find the numerical values of m and n.
　(b) A ball was thrown vertically upwards so that its height h metres above the ground, t seconds after it had been thrown, was given by the formula
$$h=7+11t-5t^2.$$
Find (i) the height above the ground from which the ball was thrown, (ii) the two values of t for which the ball was 9 metres above the ground. [C]

28　Solve the equation
$$\frac{3x+2}{x+2}=x.$$

29　(i) Find without indices the values of
$$(\tfrac{1}{2})^{-3},\ (3^{-1})^2,\ (4^{-1})^{-2}.$$

34

(ii) Solve the equation $2x^2 - 9x + 6 = 0$, giving your answers correct to 2 decimal places. [L]

30 If $h = \sqrt{\left[\dfrac{3d(L-d)}{8}\right]}$, express L in terms of h and d. [L]

31 (a) The volume of a cube is $x^3\,\text{cm}^3$.

(i) What is the length of each of its edges?

(ii) The length of each edge is reduced by 10%. Write down, in terms of x, the measurements of the 'reduced cube'.

(iii) Find the percentage decrease in the volume of the original cube when the lengths of its edges are reduced by 10%.

(b) Given that $T = 2\pi\sqrt{\dfrac{l}{g}}$, find T when $\pi = 3\tfrac{1}{7}$, $l = 98$ and $g = 32$.

(c) (i) Factorise $x^2 + 2xy + y^2$.

(ii) Use your result in (i) to find the value of $x^2 + y^2$ when $x + y = 9$ and $xy = 9$. [M]

32 Solve the simultaneous equations $x^2 - y^2 = 22$,
$$x - y = 11.$$ [L]

33 Find (a) the range of values of x for which $5x - 3 < x + 1$,

(b) the range of values of x for which $x^2 < 9$.

Indicate both these ranges on a real number line, making it clear which is which, and use your result to express the set
$$\{x : 5x - 3 < x + 1\} \cap \{x : x^2 < 9\}$$
as a single set in the form $\{x : a < x < b\}$. [L]

34 Solve the equations $\qquad x = 2y$
$$(x + y)^2 = 4.$$ [L]

35 The speed of a motor boat in still water is x km/h. A river is flowing at 6 km/h. Write down expressions for the times, in hours, taken by the motor boat to travel a distance of 5 km in the river (a) upstream, (b) downstream.

If the total time taken by the boat to travel 5 km upstream and immediately back to its starting point is 2 hours, form an equation for x and solve it.

Hence calculate the time taken by the boat to travel the 5 km upstream. [L]

Section 5
Functions, graphs and elementary calculus

The members of one set are often related to the members of another set. Such relations can be illustrated by a mapping diagram, four of which are shown in Figures 5.1, 5.2, 5.3 and 5.4.

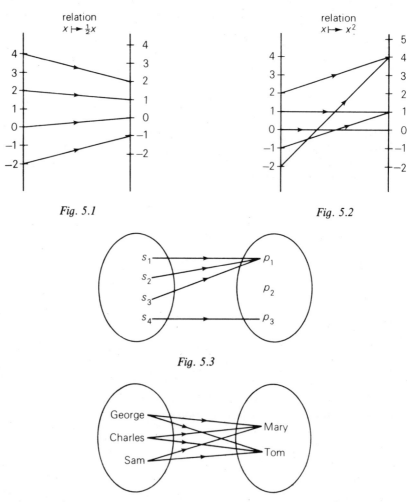

Fig. 5.1

Fig. 5.2

Fig. 5.3

Fig. 5.4

In Figure 5.1, the relation is called one–one; each element in the first set is related to one and only one element in the second set and each element in the second set is related to one and only one element in the first set.

In Figure 5.2 the relation could be called two–one; in general, there are two elements in the first set related to each element in the second set, with the exception of zero.

The elements s_1, s_2, s_3 . . . of the first set in Figure 5.3 are packs of sausages, one distinguished from another by a code stamped on each pack, and the elements of the second set p_1, p_2, p_3 . . . are the people who packaged the sausages, the relation being described by the words 'is packed by'. This relation is many–one.

In Figure 5.4 the relation 'is the son of' referred to three brothers as the first set and their parents as the second set is many–many.

For the relations shown in Figures 5.1, 5.2 and 5.3, each element of the first set has been associated with just *one* element of the second set. This fact can be checked at once from the mapping diagrams by observing that only *one* line links each element of the first set to some element in the second set. Each of these three relations are called **functions**; the first set is called the **domain** and the second set is called the **codomain**. It should be noted also that not all elements in the codomain need have a corresponding element in the domain but that every element in the domain must have one and only one element in the codomain related to it.

Many–many relations like the one illustrated in Figure 5.4 are not called functions because some or all of the elements in the first set correspond to more than one element in the second set.

Functional notation

The following notation is used to describe the functions shown in Figures 5.1 and 5.2,

$$f : x \mapsto \tfrac{1}{2}x, \text{ for } x \in \mathbb{R},$$
$$g : x \mapsto x^2, \text{ for } x \in \mathbb{R}.$$

In general, the symbol $f(x)$ is used to represent the image of the element x under the function f.

For every element x in the domain, a corresponding element $f(x)$ will result in the codomain. The complete set of these image elements for which $f(x)$ is a typical member is called the **range** of f.

Cartesian graphs

The cartesian graphs of the functions f and g are shown in Figures 5.5 and 5.6.

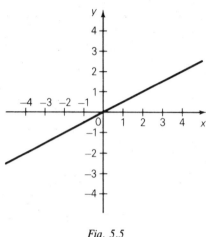

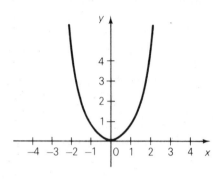

Fig. 5.5 | Fig. 5.6

The graph of f is the line $y = \frac{1}{2}x$.
The domain of f is the set $\mathbb{R}$.
The range of f is the set $\mathbb{R}$.

The graph of g is the curve, called a parabola, whose equation is $y = x^2$.
The domain of g is the set $\mathbb{R}$.
The range of g is the set $\mathbb{R}_0^+$.

Composite functions

The functions f and g, shown in mapping diagrams in Figures 5.1 and 5.2 and as cartesian graphs in Figures 5.5 and 5.6, can be combined to form composite functions as illustrated in the following examples.

Example 1: The composite function gf is given by $gf(x) = g(\frac{1}{2}x) = \frac{1}{4}x^2$ and written as $gf: x \mapsto \frac{1}{4}x^2$, for $x \in \mathbb{R}$.

Note: gf means 'do f first then g'.

Example 2: The composite function fg is given by $fg(x) = f(x^2) = \frac{1}{2}x^2$ and written as $fg: x \mapsto \frac{1}{2}x^2$, for $x \in \mathbb{R}$.

Note: fg means 'do g first then f'.

Example 3: The composite function ff, or f^2, is given by $ff(x) = f(\frac{1}{2}x) = \frac{1}{4}x$, and is written as $ff: x \mapsto \frac{1}{4}x$, for $x \in \mathbb{R}$.

Inverse functions

Consider the functions $f: x \mapsto \frac{1}{2}x$, for $x \in \mathbb{R}$,
$h: x \mapsto 2x$, for $x \in \mathbb{R}$.

The composite functions fh and hf are given by

fh (x) = f $(2x)$ = x, that is fh $: x \mapsto x$ and

hf (x) = h $(\frac{1}{2}x)$ = x, that is hf $: x \mapsto x$.

The function h is called the **inverse function of f**, written as f^{-1}.

Example: *For the function* f: $x \mapsto \dfrac{x}{x+1}$, *defined in* $\{x : x \in \mathbb{R}, x \neq -1\}$,

define the inverse function of f *in the same manner.*

f may be considered as a mapping $x \to y$ where $y = \dfrac{x}{x+1}$.

We require the mapping $y \to x$.

$$y = \frac{x}{x+1} \Rightarrow y(x+1) = x \Rightarrow yx + y = x \Rightarrow x(1-y) = y \Rightarrow x = \frac{y}{1-y}$$

We write $f^{-1} : x \mapsto \dfrac{x}{1-x}$ $\{x : x \in \mathbb{R}, x \neq 1\}$.

Note: An inverse function f^{-1} exists for a function f only when f itself is one–one.

Cartesian graphs of f and f^{-1}, where $f : x \to \frac{1}{2}x$, for $x \in \mathbb{R}$, are shown in Figure 5.7.

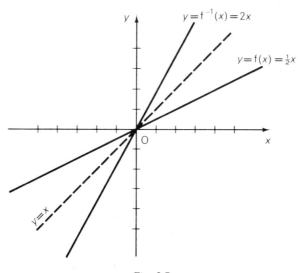

Fig. 5.7

The graph of f is the line $y = \frac{1}{2}x$ and the graph of f^{-1} is the line $y = 2x$ as shown in Figure 5.7. The inverse function's graph can be found by reflecting the graph of f in the line $y = x$.

The reader should note that the function $g : x \mapsto x^2$, as defined, does not

39

have an inverse function because the mapping is not one–one. The inverse **relation** is defined by $g^{-1}: x \mapsto \pm\sqrt{x}$.

Variation

Direct variation

A quantity p is said to vary directly as a quantity q if the ratio $\dfrac{p}{q}$ stays unchanged in value (called a constant) as p and q each take a number of different values. We write $p = kq$, where k is a constant. The notation $y \propto x$ means y varies directly as x.

Inverse variation

A quantity p is said to vary inversely as a quantity q if the product pq stays unchanged in value as p and q each take a number of different values. We write $p \propto \dfrac{1}{q}$ or $p = \dfrac{k}{q}$, where k is a constant.

Example: *Given that s is directly proportional to t^2 and that $s = 3$ when $t = 4$, find s in terms of t.*

We know that $s = kt^2$, where k is a constant.

We also are given that $s = 3$ when $t = 4$, hence $3 = 16k$ and $k = \dfrac{3}{16}$.

Therefore

$$s = \frac{3t^2}{16}.$$

Figure 5.8 shows graphs of cases in variation which should be specially noted.

The construction and use of algebraic graphs

The gradient of a line and of a curve

The gradients of the lines shown in Figure 5.9 are $\dfrac{b}{a}$ and $-\dfrac{d}{c}$. The gradient of the curve at the point P in Figure 5.10 is the same as the gradient of the tangent at P to the curve. In practical questions the tangent is often ruled by eye and the gradient estimated from this line. If the equation of the curve is known, a precise value of the gradient to the curve at any point can be found by differentiation.

If $y = x^n$, the rate of change of y with respect to x is given by

$\dfrac{dy}{dx} = n x^{n-1}$, called the gradient function of $y = x^n$.

40

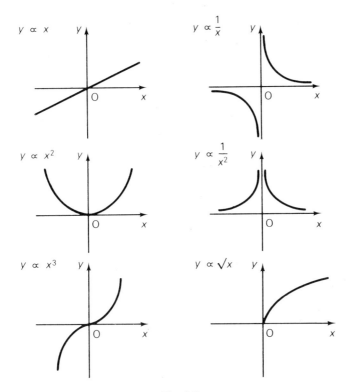

Fig. 5.8

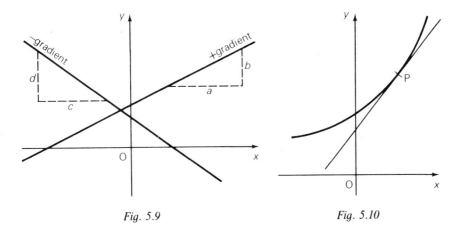

Fig. 5.9   Fig. 5.10

Different forms of the equation of a straight line

1. $y = mx + c$ is the equation of the line with gradient m and y intercept c.

2. $y - k = m(x - h)$ is the equation of the line with gradient m, passing through the point (h, k).

41

3. $\dfrac{x}{a} + \dfrac{y}{b} = 1$ is the equation of the line passing through $(a, 0)$ on the x-axis and $(0, b)$ on the y-axis.

When sketching the graph of a line whose equation is given, find the points where the graph crosses the coordinate axes, checking the accuracy of your sketch by verifying that a third point also lies on the line.

Linear inequations

The line $y = mx + c$ divides the plane into two half-planes; $y > mx + c$ is the relation satisfied by all points above the line, $y < mx + c$ is the relation satisfied by all points below the line. The inequations $x < k$ and $x > k$ are represented by the half-planes to the left of the line $x = k$ and to the right of the line $x = k$ respectively.

   If several inequations are satisfied simultaneously, a region of the plane will be defined. For each inequation the line representing the corresponding equation should be drawn, and if the defined half-plane is left unshaded, the final region will appear unshaded. If an inequation is strict, e.g. $y > 2x + 5$, a broken line is drawn to indicate that points on the line are not included in the solution set.

Example 1: *Show in a sketch the region A defined by the inequations:* $y \leqslant x$, $x < 4$, *and* $y + x > -2$

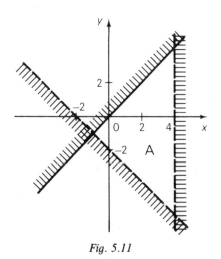

Fig. 5.11

The three boundary lines are drawn; $x = 4$ and $x + y = -2$ are broken.
Figure 5.11 shows the unshaded region A.

Example 2: *Write down four inequations which define the unshaded region B in Figure 5.12.*

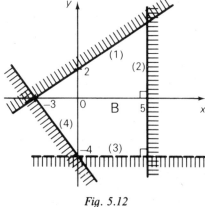

Fig. 5.12

Line (1) has gradient $\tfrac{2}{3}$ and intercept on the y-axis of 2; its equation is $y = \tfrac{2}{3}x + 2$ $[3y = 2x + 6]$. Line (2) has equation $x = 5$, line (3) has equation $y = -4$ and line (4) has equation $y = -\tfrac{4}{3}x - 4$ $[m = -\tfrac{4}{3}, c = -4]$. The inequations are: $y \leqslant \tfrac{2}{3}x + 2$, $x \leqslant 5$, $y > -4$ and $y \geqslant -\tfrac{4}{3}x - 4$.

42

When sketching or drawing the graph of a curve, the following steps should be taken:

(a) work out a table of values of y for your chosen values of x,
(b) choose scales which are as large as possible, but fit the paper,
(c) plot the points from your table,
(d) check again for any points which seem to spoil the 'smoothness' of the plots,
(e) join successive points with a smooth curve.

Some useful results from calculus

y	$\dfrac{dy}{dx}$	$\int y\,dx$
$k = $ constant	0	$kx + C$
x^2	$2x$	$\dfrac{x^3}{3} + C$
x^3	$3x^2$	$\dfrac{x^4}{4} + C$
$\dfrac{1}{x^2} = x^{-2}$	$-2x^{-3} = -\dfrac{2}{x^3}$	$-x^{-1} + C = -\dfrac{1}{x} + C$

Figure 5.13 shows the finite region, area A, which is enclosed by the curve $y = f(x)$, the x-axis, the lines $x = a$ and $x = b$.

$$A = \int_a^b f(x)\,dx$$

$$V = \pi \int_a^b [f(x)]^2\,dx,$$

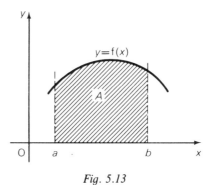

Fig. 5.13

where V is the volume generated when the region of area A is rotated about Ox through four right angles.

Example 1: *Given that* $y = x - 4 + \dfrac{11}{x}$, *find the values of y when x* $= 1, 2, 3,$ *4, 5, 6 and 7, writing the results in the form of a table.*

(a) *Using a scale of* 1 *unit* $\equiv 2$ *cm on each axis, draw the graph of the curve whose equation is* $y = x - 4 + \dfrac{11}{x}$ *for* $1 \leqslant x \leqslant 7$.

43

(b) Use your graph to estimate the minimum value of y and the value of x for which this occurs.

(c) Draw, by eye, tangent at the point P on the curve at which x = 1·5 and estimate the gradient of this tangent.

(d) Use differentiation to check your estimates found in (b) and (c).

x	1	2	3	4	5	6	7
-4	-4	-4	-4	-4	-4	-4	-4
$\frac{11}{x}$	11	5·5	3·67	2·75	2·2	1·83	1·57
$y = x - 4 + \frac{11}{x}$	8	3·5	2·67	2·75	3·2	3·83	4·57

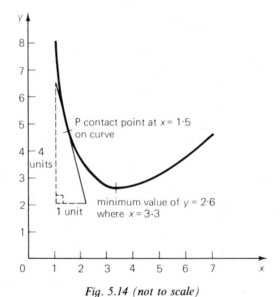

Fig. 5.14 (not to scale)

An indication only is given for the solution to (a), (b) and (c). The reader is expected to draw an accurate graph to check the results using Figure 5.14 as a guide only.

(b) Minimum point (3·3, 2·6).

(c) Estimate of gradient of tangent at P is $-\dfrac{4}{1} = -4$.

(d) $y = x - 4 + \dfrac{11}{x} = x - 4 + 11x^{-1}$

$\Rightarrow \dfrac{dy}{dx} = 1 - 0 - 11x^{-2} = 1 - \dfrac{11}{x^2}.$

The minimum value of y will occur when $\dfrac{dy}{dx} = 0$,

that is when $1 - \dfrac{11}{x^2} = 0 \Rightarrow x^2 = 11 \Rightarrow x = \pm\sqrt{11} \approx \pm 3\cdot32.$

When $x = \sqrt{11}$, $y = \sqrt{11} - 4 + \dfrac{11}{\sqrt{11}} \approx 2{\cdot}63$.

The minimum value of y is 2·63 and occurs when x = 3·32.

When $x = 1{\cdot}5$, $\dfrac{dy}{dx} = 1 - \dfrac{11}{1{\cdot}5^2} \approx -3{\cdot}9$.

Gradient of tangent at P ≈ −3·9.

Example 2: *A particle P, moving in a straight line, passes through a point O. At time t seconds, where t ≥ 0, the distance, s metres, of P from O is given by s = 3t + 2t³. Find the velocity and acceleration of P when t = 3.*

Since velocity is rate of change of displacement with respect to time, the velocity, v m/s, of P is given by $v = \dfrac{ds}{dt} = 3 + 6t^2$.

When $t = 3$, $v = 3 + 6 \times 3^2 = 57$.
When t = 3, the velocity of P is 57 m/s.

Since acceleration is rate of change of velocity with respect to time, the acceleration a m/s² of P is given by $a = \dfrac{dv}{dt} = 0 + 12t$.

When $t = 3$, $a = 12 \times 3 = 36$.
When t = 3, the acceleration of P is 36 m/s².

Example 3: *Find the coordinates of the points at which the curve with equation y = 4x − x² crosses the x-axis. Calculate the area of the finite region enclosed between this curve and the x-axis, and the volume generated when this region is rotated through 360° about the x-axis.*

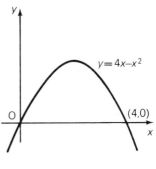

Fig. 5.15

Curve will cross x-axis when $y = 0$, that is

$$4x - x^2 = 0$$
$$\Rightarrow x(4 - x) = 0$$
$$\Rightarrow x = 0 \text{ or } x = 4.$$

The points are the origin and $(4, 0)$ and are shown in Figure 5.15 with the curve.

$$\text{Area} = \int_0^4 (4x - x^2)\, dx = \left[2x^2 - \frac{x^3}{3} \right]_0^4 = 32 - \frac{64}{3} = 10\frac{2}{3}.$$

$$\text{Volume} = \pi \int_0^4 (4x - x^2)^2\, dx = \pi \int_0^4 (16x^2 - 8x^3 + x^4)\, dx$$

$$= \pi \left[\frac{16x^3}{3} - 2x^4 + \frac{x^5}{5} \right]_0^4$$

$$= \pi \left[\frac{1024}{3} - 512 + \frac{1024}{5} \right]$$

$$= \frac{512}{15}\pi.$$

45

Exercise 5.1

1 If $f:x \mapsto x^2 - 4x$, find
   (i) the range set, whose domain set is $\{-1, 0, 1\}$,
   (ii) the domain set, whose range set is $\{-3, 0\}$.   [L]

2 The function f maps x on to $3x + 2$.
   (a) Find the image of each of the following: (i) 4, (ii) 0, (iii) $-\frac{1}{2}$,
   (iv) -2.
   (b) If the domain of f is the real number line from -2 to 5, write down the range of f.   [M]

3 If $f:x \mapsto 2x + 3$ and $g:x \mapsto 4x + k$, find the value of k such that fg and gf are the same mapping.
   If k has this value, find the value of x such that $fg(x) = 25$.   [L]

4 Given that $f:x \mapsto 3x$ and $g:x \mapsto x - 2$, find the values of x and y for which
   (a) $f:x \mapsto 12$, (b) $f^{-1}g:y \mapsto 2$.   [L]

5 (a) Given that $h:x \mapsto Ax^2 + B$, and that $h(3) = 7$ and $h'(3) = 6$, where h' is the derived function of h, find the values of A and B.
   (b) Explain why h^{-1} is not a function, but $(h')^{-1}$ is a function.   [L]

6 For a positive integer x, $f(x)$ denotes the sum of the prime numbers, excluding 1, which are less than x. For example, $f(7) = 2 + 3 + 5 = 10$ and $f(8) = 2 + 3 + 5 + 7 = 17$.
   (i) Find $f(12)$.
   (ii) Find a value of x, given that $f(x) = 58$.
   (iii) State the value of x other than 31 for which $f(x) = f(31)$.   [C]

7 Two functions, $f:x \mapsto \dfrac{1}{1-x}$ and $g:x \mapsto \dfrac{x-1}{x}$, are defined for $x \in \{-1, \frac{1}{2}, 2\}$.
   (i) Copy and complete the following arrow diagrams:

   (a) f   (b) f^2 (c) g
   $-1 \rightarrow \frac{1}{2}$ $-1 \rightarrow$ $-1 \rightarrow$
   $\frac{1}{2} \rightarrow$ $\frac{1}{2} \rightarrow$ $\frac{1}{2} \rightarrow$
   $2 \rightarrow$ $2 \rightarrow$ $2 \rightarrow$

   (ii) Show that $gf:x \mapsto x$, for all $x \in \{-1, \frac{1}{2}, 2\}$.   [L]

8 Functions f and g are defined for all values of x by
$$f:x \mapsto \frac{x}{2} + 1 \text{ and } g:x \mapsto x^2 - 1.$$
   Write down the definition, in terms of x, of the composition function gf. Find the set of values of x for which $g(f(x)) \leqslant 0$.   [AEB]

9 If y is directly proportional to x, and $y = 6$ when $x = 2$,
   (i) express y in terms of x,   (ii) find the value of x when $y = 12$.   [C]

10 The straight line with equation $\dfrac{x}{a} + \dfrac{y}{b} = 1$ passes through the points $(2, 0)$ and $(0, -5)$. Find a and b and the gradient of the line.   [C]

11 Given that $t = \dfrac{k}{v^2}$ and $t = 25$ when $v = 2$, find the value of k. With this value of k calculate the value of t when $v = 3$.   [L]

12 Two positive variables x and y are such that $y = \dfrac{k}{x^2}$.
   Illustrate this relation by a sketch graph.
   Given that $y = 8$ when $x = 0.5$, obtain the value of k.   [L]

13 A straight line passes through the points $(0, 3)$ and $(6, 6)$. Find
   (i) the gradient of the line,
   (ii) the equation of the line.   [C]

14 Using a scale of 1 cm for 1 unit on each axis and using the same axes for both graphs, draw the graphs of the following relations for values of x from 0 to 10 only.
(i) $y = 8 - x$, (ii) $y = x + 2$.
(a) On your graph paper, indicate the point A at which $8 - x = x + 2$. State the coordinates of A.
(b) Shade the region of your graph paper for which y is less than $8 - x$ but greater than $x + 2$.
(c) Draw the line which passes through (2, 0) and (10, 4). Find the equation of this line.   [M]

15

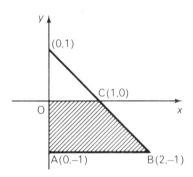

Fig. 5.16

O is the origin and A, B and C are points $(0, -1)$, $(2, -1)$ and $(1, 0)$ respectively.
Write down the four inequalities which define the shaded area ABCO including its boundary.   [C]

16 Indicate clearly on a diagram the region defined by $y \geqslant 0$, $x + y \leqslant 2$ and $y \leqslant 2x - 1$.   [C]

17 Given that $y = 3x^2 + 3 + \dfrac{1}{x^2}$, find $\dfrac{dy}{dx}$.   [L]

18 If $\dfrac{dy}{dx} = 2 + \dfrac{1}{x^2}$, and $y = 2$ when $x = 1$, find an expression for y in terms of x.   [L]

19 Given that $\dfrac{dy}{dx} = 2x - 5$ and that $y = 3$ when $x = 0$, express y in terms of x and hence calculate the value of y when $x = 1$.   [JMB]

20 The region bounded by the x-axis, the lines $x = 1$ and $x = 3$ and the curve $y = x + \dfrac{3}{x}$ is rotated completely about the x-axis. Show that the volume of the solid of revolution formed is $\dfrac{80\pi}{3}$.   [JMB]

21 Given that $A = 5y^3 - 6y + 1$, calculate the value of $\dfrac{dA}{dy}$ when $y = 2$. [JMB]

22 Calculate the value of $\displaystyle\int_{1}^{2} 6x \, dx$.   [JMB]

23 Evaluate

$$\int_{0}^{5} (x^4 - 3x^2) \, dx.$$ [JMB]

24 The curve $y = \dfrac{x^2}{2} - 2x + k$, where k is a constant, passes through the point (6, 13). Calculate
   (i) the value of k,
   (ii) the gradient of the tangent to the curve at the point where the curve crosses the y-axis,
   (iii) the coordinates of the turning point on the curve, determining whether the curve has a maximum or minimum turning point.
   Hence *sketch* the curve.   [AEB]

25 O and P are points on a line. A particle moves along the line in such a way that, t seconds after it is at O, its velocity is v cm/s, where $v = kt - t^2$ and k is a constant. At the time when $t = 6$, the particle is momentarily at rest at P. Find (i) the value of k, (ii) the distance OP, (iii) the average speed of the particle between O and P, (iv) the acceleration of the particle when it is at P.   [L]

Exercise 5.2

1 The mappings f and g are defined as follows:
$$f: x \mapsto x - 3,$$
$$g: x \mapsto x^2.$$
Express in the form $x \mapsto \ldots \ldots$
   (i) the inverse mapping f^{-1},
   (ii) the inverse mapping g^{-1}, (This is a 1-to-2 mapping as also are (v) and (vi) below.)
   (iii) gf,
   (iv) fgf,
   (v) $(gf)^{-1}$,
   (vi) $(fgf)^{-1}$.
Find a mapping h such that hgf: $x \mapsto x^2 - 6x + 3$.
Find $(hgf)^{-1}$, and hence, or otherwise, solve the equation
$$x^2 - 6x + 3 = 2,$$
giving each answer correct to 2 decimal places.   [L]

2 Functions f and g are defined so that
$$f: x \mapsto x^2, \quad g: x \mapsto ax - 2, \text{ where } a \text{ is a constant.}$$
Define the mappings fg and gf.
   If $a = 2$, find values of x for which $fg(x) = gf(x)$, and state the range of values of x for which $fg(x) < gf(x)$.
   If $a = 1$, show that there is only one value of x for which $fg(x) = gf(x)$, and find this value.
   Show that $fg(x)$ and $gf(x)$ cannot be equal for any value of x if $a - 0$.
                                                                                [L]

3 The functions f and g map x onto $3x - 2$ and $2x^2 + 1$ respectively. Show that fg maps x onto $6x^2 + 1$, and find the mapping of the function gf.
   A third function, h, maps x onto $ax + b$, where a and b are positive constants, and is such that fgh maps x onto $6x^2 + 12x + 7$.
   Find the values of a and b and also that of fgh (-2).
   Find the two values of x for which fgh$(x) = 25$.   [L]

4 Draw up a table of values for the function $2x^2 + x - 1$ taking values of x at intervals of $\frac{1}{2}$ from $x = -2$ to $x = 1\frac{1}{2}$. Using a scale of 2 cm to represent 1 unit on both axes, draw the graph of $y = 2x^2 + x - 1$.
   With the same scale and axes draw the graph of $y = \frac{1}{2}(x + 1)$.
   Find from your graphs
   (a) the solutions of the equation $4x^2 + x - 3 = 0$,
   (b) the range of values of x for which $\frac{1}{2}(x + 1)$ is greater than $2x^2 + x - 1$.
                                                                                [L]

5 Draw the graph of $y = 5 + 4x - x^2$, for values of x from 0 to 5, using a scale of 2 cm to 1 unit on each axis.

By integration, or by an approximate method which may involve making use of the graph, find the area enclosed between the graph and the coordinate axes.

State what quantity is represented by this area, and in what units it would be given, in each of the following cases:

(a) y is the velocity in metres per second of a moving body at a time x seconds after observations begin,

(b) y is the horizontal cross-sectional area, in square centimetres, of a body, measured x cm above the base. [L]

6 A rectangular field whose sides are of length x metres and y metres has an area of 1000 m². Copy and complete the following table:

x	15	20	25	30	40	50	60	70	80
y	66·7	50		33·3	25		16·7	14·3	

Using 2 cm to represent 10 metres on each axis, plot all the points in the table and join them by a smooth curve.

A rectangular field whose area is 1000 m² has a perimeter of 150 m. Write down the perimeter of the rectangle in terms of x and y. Hence find, by adding a straight line to your graph, the possible values of x for this field. [C]

7 Draw the graph of $y = \frac{1}{2}(x^2 + 2x - 5)$ for values of x from -3 to $+3$, taking 2 cm to represent 1 unit on each axis. Use your graph to estimate the values of x for which $\frac{1}{2}(x^2 + 2x - 5) = -1·75$.

Using the same axes and scale draw the graph of $y = \frac{1}{5}(3x - 4)$. Write down and simplify the equation, the solutions of which are given by the points of intersection of the two graphs, and estimate the solutions of this equation. [L]

8 The graph below shows the speed v metres per second of a car t seconds after a given instant.

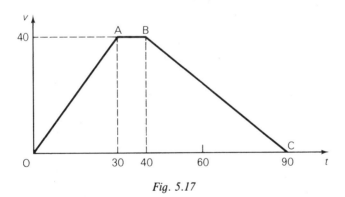

Fig. 5.17

(a) State what the gradient of the line OA represents. Give the value of the gradient.

(b) Calculate how far the car travels in the ten seconds from $t = 30$ to $t = 40$.

(c) Calculate the speed of the car when $t = 60$.

(d) Find the total distance travelled by the car in the 90 seconds shown on the graph. [L]

9 Using a scale of 2 cm to represent one unit on the x-axis and 4 cm to represent one unit on the y-axis, draw the graph of $y = \dfrac{4}{x^2} + 1$ for values of x from $x = 1$ to $x = 5$ at unit intervals.

On the same set of axes and using the same scales draw the graph of $y = \dfrac{x}{2}$.

Write down and simplify the equation in x satisfied at the point of intersection of the curve and the straight line and read off the approximate solution of this equation from the graph. [AEB]

10 The eggs produced by a poultry farm are graded as small, medium or large. On a particular day $x \%$ of the eggs are small, $y \%$ medium and the remainder large.
(i) State why $x + y \leqslant 100$.
(ii) The percentage of small eggs is at least twice the percentage of medium eggs. Use this information to write down another inequality satisfied by x *and* y.
(iii) Given also that the percentage of large eggs is not greater than three times the percentage of medium eggs, show that $x + 4y \geqslant 100$.

The point (x, y) represents $x \%$ of small eggs and $y \%$ of medium eggs. Using 2 cm to represent 10% on each axis, construct accurately on graph paper, and shade, the region in which (x, y) must lie.

Using your graph, find (a) the least percentage of small eggs, (b) the limits between which the percentage of small eggs must lie if 20% of the eggs are medium. [C]

11 A rectangle of length y cm and width x cm is to be drawn subject to the following four conditions.
(i) The length must be greater than the width.
(ii) The length must be less than three times the width.
(iii) The length of the perimeter must be greater than 200 cm.
(iv) The length of the perimeter must be less than 280 cm.
Write down four inequalities involving both x and y.

On graph paper, indicate the set of points with coordinates (x, y) which satisfies these inequalities. (Use a scale of 1 cm to represent 10 cm on each axis.)

Given that the area of the rectangle is to be 2400 cm^2, find one possible pair of integral values of x and y. [JMB]

12 A garage owner decides that he would like to expand his business by starting a car rental enterprise offering a selection of medium and small cars for hire. He intends to purchase at least three small cars, but he knows that it is not worth his while to buy more than a total of twelve cars. He also reckons that the ratio of medium cars to small cars should not be greater than $3:2$. Each small car costs him £2500, whilst a medium one costs £3500, but he has a maximum of £35 000 to spend.

Taking the number of small cars he could buy as x, and the number of medium cars as y, explain why $2y \leqslant 3x$ and $5x + 7y \leqslant 70$. Write down two other inequalities which x, y must satisfy. By using a scale of 1 cm to represent one unit on each axis, represent this information in a cartesian graph.

Given that the average profit per day on each small car is £2, whereas for each medium car it is £3, find the values of x and y which would maximise his profit. [JMB]

13 P and Q are two points on the curve
$$y = x^3 + 6x + 2.$$
The x-coordinate of P is 1 and the x-coordinate of Q is 4. Show that the gradient of the chord PQ is 27.

R is a point on the curve between P and Q at which the tangent to the curve is parallel to PQ. Calculate the x-coordinate of R. (Your answer may be left in surd form.)

Calculate also the coordinates of points on the curve at which the gradient is nine times the x-coordinate at these points. [JMB]

14 A particle moving in a straight line starts from a fixed point O. After t seconds it reaches a point P where $OP = x$ metres. If $x = t^3 - 2t^2 + t$, find expressions in terms of t for the velocity and the acceleration of the particle. Calculate
(a) the values of t for which the velocity of the particle is zero,
(b) the distance between the positions of the particle at these times,
(c) the velocity of the particle when its acceleration is zero. [L]

15 A particle P moves along the x-axis in such a way that, t seconds after it leaves the origin O, its displacement $x = 6t^2 - t^3$.
(i) Show that the particle returns to O when $t = 6$, and find the value of x when $t = 3$.
(ii) Find the speed with which the particle returns to O.
(iii) Find the value of t (other than 0) for which the particle is momentarily at rest, and hence show that during the first 6 seconds of motion $x \leqslant 32$.
(iv) Find the maximum speed of the particle in the direction Ox. [L]

16 (a) The curve whose equation is $y = Ax^2 + \dfrac{B}{x}$ passes through the points $(1, 9)$ and $(-1, -7)$. Find the values of A and B, and show that the curve also passes through $(4, 18)$.
(b) Calculate the value of x when $y = 0$.
(c) Show that the gradient of the tangent to the curve at the point $(1, 9)$ is -6.
(d) Find the x-coordinate of the point at which the tangent to the curve at $(1, 9)$ meets the x-axis.
(e) Calculate correct to one decimal place the x-coordinate of the point at which the gradient of the curve is zero. [L]

17 Show that the line $y = 3$ cuts the curve $y = 4x - x^2$ at the points $(1, 3)$ and $(3, 3)$. Calculate the area of the region enclosed by the curve and the line $y = 3$.
The region enclosed by the curve from $x = 0$ to $x = 1$, the x-axis and the line $x = 1$ is rotated completely about the x-axis. Calculate the volume of the solid of revolution generated, leaving your answer as a multiple of π. [JMB]

18 Calculate the coordinates of
(a) the points where the curve $y = -x^2 + 8x - 12$ cuts the axes,
(b) the maximum point on the curve.
Without further calculation, sketch the curve, indicating these points clearly.
Calculate the area bounded by the x-axis and the arc of the curve which lies above the x-axis. [L]

19 Calculate the coordinates of the turning points of the graph of
$$y = x^3 - 3x^2 - 9x + 23$$
distinguishing between maximum and minimum points.
P is the only point on this curve at which the gradient is -12. Calculate the coordinates of P.
The tangent at P crosses the x-axis at Q. Calculate the coordinates of Q. [JMB]

20 The velocity v m/s of a particle moving in a straight line is given by
$$v = 18t - 3t^2 \quad (0 \leqslant t \leqslant 3)$$
where t is the time (in seconds) measured from the instant when motion begins.
Show that the acceleration is zero when $t = 3$ and find the distance travelled in the first 3 seconds.
For values of t in the interval $3 \leqslant t \leqslant 6$, the velocity v m/s is given by
$$v = 6t + 81/t^2.$$
Show that there is no abrupt change in the velocity or the acceleration. Find the distance travelled during the interval $3 \leqslant t \leqslant 6$. [L]

Section 6
Simple geometrical properties and plane transformations

The following notes and diagrams list and illustrate the main facts you will need to know and use in geometrical work.

Acute angles lie between 0° and 90°.
Obtuse angles lie between 90° and 180°.
Reflex angles lie between 180° and 360°.
Complementary angles add up to 90°.
Supplementary angles add up to 180°.

Angles at a point formed by the intersection of two straight lines
$a+b = 180°$, etc.
$a = c$ and $b = d$ (vertically opposite)
$a+b+c+d = 360°$

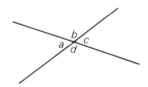

Fig. 6.1

Angles formed by parallel lines and a transversal
$x = y$ (alternate angles)
$u = z$ (corresponding angles)
$x+z = 180°$ (interior angles)

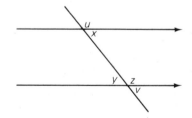

Fig. 6.2

Triangle
$p+q+r = 180°$
$p+q = s$

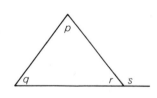

Fig. 6.3

Polygon (n sides)

Sum of interior angles = $(180n - 360)$ degrees.

Sum of exterior angles = $360°$.

If all sides equal and all interior angles equal, polygon is called **regular.**

Conditions for congruency of triangles
1. $a = x$, $b = y$, $c = z$.   (SSS)
2. $a = x$, $b = y$, $C = Z$.   (SAS)
3. $a = x$, $A = X$, $B = Y$.   (AAS)
4. $A = X = 90°$, $a = x$, $b = y$. (RHS)

Fig. 6.4

Conditions for similarity of triangles
1. $A = P$, $B = Q$ (AAA)

2. $A = P$, $\dfrac{b}{q} = \dfrac{c}{r}$ (SAS)

3. $\dfrac{a}{p} = \dfrac{b}{q} = \dfrac{c}{r}$ (SSS)

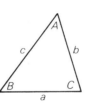
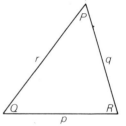

Fig. 6.5

Triangles

Isosceles triangle

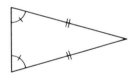

Fig. 6.6

Two sides equal, the angles opposite these sides equal.
One axis of symmetry.

Equilateral triangle

Fig. 6.7

All sides equal, all angles $60°$.
Rotational symmetry of order 3;
three axes of symmetry.

Pythagoras' Theorem

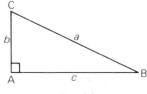

Fig. 6.8

If $A = 90°$, $a^2 = b^2 + c^2$.

Converse:

If $a^2 = b^2 + c^2$, then $A = 90°$.

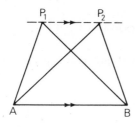

Fig. 6.9

Area of a triangle

$$= \tfrac{1}{2} \times \text{base} \times \text{height.}$$

Triangles with same base and with third vertex on a line parallel to the base are equal in area.

$\triangle ABP_1 = \triangle ABP_2$ in area.

Loci

The perpendicular bisector locus

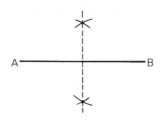

Fig. 6.10

Note: All points on the dotted line are equidistant from A and B.

The angle bisector locus

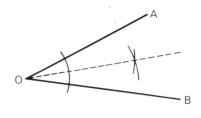

Fig. 6.11

Note: All points on the dotted line are equidistant from OA and OB.

Quadrilaterals

Trapezium

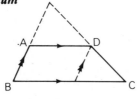

Fig. 6.12

Definition: One pair of opposite sides parallel.
No axes of symmetry.
A trapezium is the difference of two similar triangles OR the sum of a parallelogram and a triangle.

Isosceles Trapezium

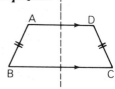

Fig. 6.13

Definition: A trapezium whose non-parallel sides are equal in length, AB = DC.
Angle properties:
B = C, A = D.
One axis of symmetry.

54

Kite

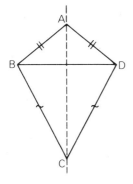

Fig. 6.14

Arrowhead
(Reflex kite)

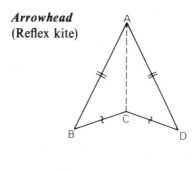

Fig. 6.15

Definition: One diagonal, AC, is an axis of symmetry.
Properties:
AB = AD, CB = CD.
angle B = angle D.
AC is perpendicular to BD.
One axis of symmetry.

Definition: As for a kite, but angle C reflex.

Properties as for kite but note AC *produced* is perpendicular to BD.

Parallelogram

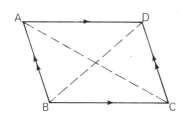

Fig. 6.16

Rhombus

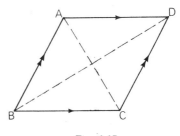

Fig. 6.17

Definition: Opposite sides parallel.
Properties:
AB = DC, AD = BC.
Opposite angles equal.
Diagonals bisect each other.
Rotational symmetry of order 2;
no axis of symmetry.

Definition: A parallelogram with all sides equal.
Properties: As for a parallelogram plus diagonals are perpendicular to each other; diagonals bisect the angles.
Rotational symmetry of order 2;
two axes of symmetry.

55

Rectangle

Definition: A parallelogram with all angles equal (90°)

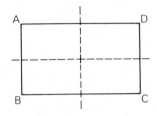

Fig. 6.18

Properties: As for a parallelogram plus the diagonals are equal in length.
Rotational symmetry of order 2; *two axes of symmetry.*

Square

Definition: A parallelogram with all sides equal and all angles equal.

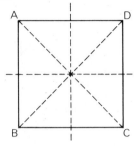

Fig. 6.19

Properties: As for a rhombus plus diagonals equal.
Rotational symmetry of order four; *four axes of symmetry.*

Circles

Radius–chord property

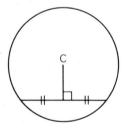

Fig. 6.20

Radius–tangent property

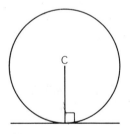

Fig. 6.21

Angle at centre double the angle at the circumference

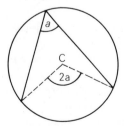

Fig. 6.22

The angle in a semicircle is a right-angle

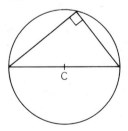

Fig. 6.23

Angles in the same segment are equal

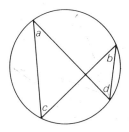

Fig. 6.24

Note: $a = b$ and $c = d$.

Angles in opposite segments are supplementary

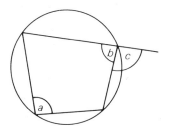

Fig. 6.25

Note: $a + b = 180°$ and $a = c$.

Intersecting chords (internal)

OA.OB = OC.OD

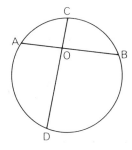

Fig. 6.26

Intersecting chords (external)

OA.OB = OC.OD = OT²

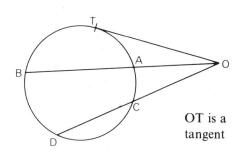

OT is a tangent

Fig. 6.27

Tangents from external point to a circle are equal in length

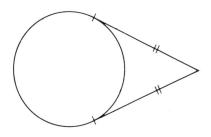

Fig. 6.28

The alternate segment property

$a = b, c = d$

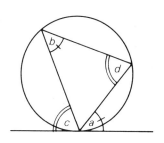

Fig. 6.29

Solutions

The following flow-chart suggests a method for solving most geometrical problems.

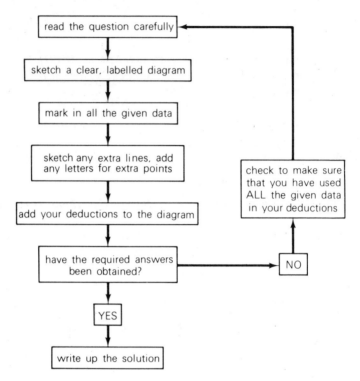

In writing solutions, each step should be backed up with a reason. The following examples illustrate this.

Example 1: *In Figure 6.30, AD is parallel to BC and AP is perpendicular to BC; AB = 11 cm, BP = 6 cm, ∠ACB = 69° and ∠ADC = 42°.*
(a) Prove that △ADC is isosceles. (b) Calculate the length of AP.

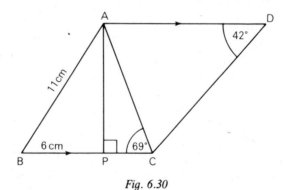

Fig. 6.30

(a) $\angle DAC = \angle ACB = 69°$ (alt. angles: AD parallel to BC)
$\qquad \angle DCA = 180° - (69° + 42°) = 69°$ (third angle of triangle)
$\qquad \Rightarrow \angle DCA = \angle DAC \Rightarrow DA = DC$ and triangle DAC is
$\qquad\qquad\qquad\qquad\qquad\qquad\qquad\qquad\qquad\qquad$ isosceles.
(b) $AB^2 = AP^2 + BP^2$ (Pythagoras)
$\qquad \Rightarrow AP = \sqrt{(11^2 - 6^2)} = \sqrt{85} \Rightarrow AP \approx 9·22\,cm.$

Example 2: *In Figure 6.31, C is the centre of the circle, ACBO is a straight line, OTS is a tangent and TC produced meets the circle again at P. Given that $\angle STA = 48°$, find (a) $\angle APT$, (b) $\angle BOT$.*

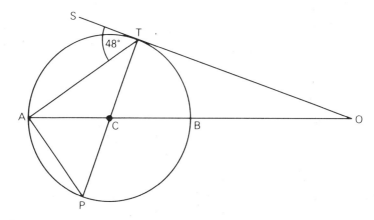

Fig. 6.31

(a) Since TA is a chord and ST is a tangent,
$\qquad \angle STA = \angle TPA = 48°$ (alternate segment property).
(b) Since CT is a radius and OTS a tangent,
$\qquad \angle OTC = 90°$ (radius perpendicular to tangent property).
$\qquad \angle ACT = 2\angle APT$ (angle at centre double that at circumference)
$\qquad\qquad = 96°.$
$\qquad \angle BOT = 96° - 90° = 6°$ (exterior angle of triangle property).

Transformation geometry

If a point P is mapped on to a point P′ under a transformation M, we write $P' = M(P)$, i.e. $M(P)$ is the image of P under M; if Q is a quadrilateral, $M(Q)$ represents the image of Q under M.

Points and lines whose positions remain unaltered under a transformation are said to be **invariant**; if the points on a line remain unaltered, the line is **point invariant**.

A transformation for which the distance between pairs of points remains unaltered is called an **isometry**; a figure and its image are congruent under an isometry.

The following transformations of the plane are illustrated by considering a $\triangle ABC$ and its image, $\triangle A'B'C'$.

Translation (T)

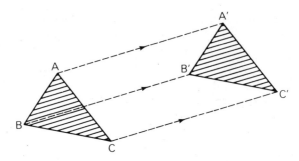

Fig. 6.32

$T(A) = A'$, $T(B) = B'$, $T(C) = C'$.
$\overrightarrow{AA'} = \overrightarrow{BB'} = \overrightarrow{CC'}$.

There are no invariant points. The order of the letters is preserved; the triangles are directly congruent.

Reflection in a line (M)

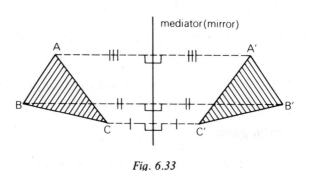

Fig. 6.33

$M(A) = A'$, $M(B) = B'$, $M(C) = C'$.

The mediator is the perpendicular bisector of AA', BB' and CC'. All points on the mediator are invariant; all lines perpendicular to the mediator are invariant. The order of the letters is reversed; the triangles are oppositely congruent.

60

Rotation about a point (R)

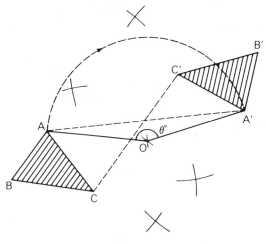

Fig. 6.34

$R(A) = A'$, $R(B) = B'$, $R(C) = C'$.

The centre of rotation O is at the point of intersection of the perpendicular bisectors of AA', BB', CC'.

If the angle of rotation is $\theta°$, (clockwise $-\theta°$), $A\hat{O}A' = B\hat{O}B' = C\hat{O}C' = \theta°$. O is the only invariant point. The order of the letters is preserved; the triangles are directly congruent.

Glide reflection (G)

A translation followed by a reflection in a line parallel to the direction of translation.

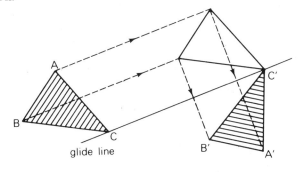

Fig. 6.35

$G(A) = A'$, $G(B) = B'$, $G(C) = C'$.

No points are invariant; the glide-line is invariant.

The above transformations are all isometries.

61

Enlargement, centre O, scale factor k (E)

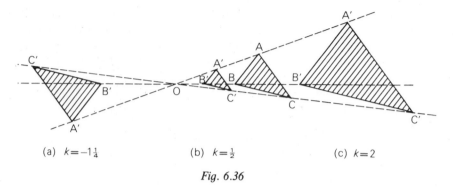

(a) $k = -1\frac{1}{4}$　　　　(b) $k = \frac{1}{2}$　　　　(c) $k = 2$

Fig. 6.36

$E(A) = A'$, $E(B) = B'$, $E(C) = C'$.

Figure 6.36 shows the effect of the enlargement, centre O, in the cases when k is (a) $-1\frac{1}{4}$, (b) $\frac{1}{2}$, (c) 2. In each case:

$$\overrightarrow{OA'} = k\overrightarrow{OA}, \quad \overrightarrow{OB'} = k\overrightarrow{OB}, \quad \overrightarrow{OC'} = k\overrightarrow{OC}, \quad \text{and}$$
$$\overrightarrow{A'C'} = k\overrightarrow{AC}, \quad \overrightarrow{A'B'} = k\overrightarrow{AB}, \quad \overrightarrow{B'C'} = k\overrightarrow{BC}.$$

The only invariant point is the centre of enlargement O.

In an enlargement the object figure and its image are similar; if the scale factor is k, the area scale factor is k^2.

An enlargement, scale factor -1, is equivalent to a half turn about the centre of enlargement.

Shear (S)

A shear is a transformation in which there is a point invariant line and all other points of the plane move parallel to this line. Figure 6.37 shows a shear in which line L is invariant. All other points move parallel to L such that all straight lines remain straight lines, and area is an invariant property. The distance between points and corresponding images is proportional to their distance from the invariant line. In Figure 6.37, if P is the mid-point of AC, then $CC' = 2PP'$. Note that Q moves to Q' under this shear.

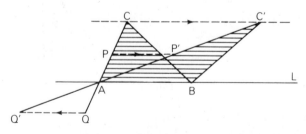

Fig. 6.37

$S(A) = A$, $S(B) = B$, $S(C) = C'$.

Stretch (U)

A stretch is a transformation in which there is a point invariant line and all other points of the plane move in a direction perpendicular to this line. If the stretch factor is k, each point is mapped onto an image whose distance from the invariant line is k times the original distance. Figure 6.38 shows $\triangle ABC$ stretched onto $\triangle ABC'$ with AB as the invariant line. Under the same stretch $\triangle APB$ maps onto $\triangle AP'B$. Area of image figure $= k$ (area of original figure).

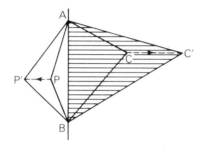

Fig. 6.38

$$U(A) = A, \quad U(B) = B, \quad U(C) = C'.$$

Example: *In Figure 6.39 $AE = 2BA$, GE is parallel to BC, DFHA is a rectangle, CAG is a straight line and $DF = \frac{3}{4}DG$. Name three successive transformations which map $\triangle ABC$ onto $\triangle AEH$, and deduce the area of $\triangle AEH$ given that the area of $\triangle ABC$ is 3 cm².*

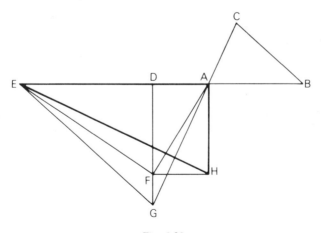

Fig. 6.39

As $\triangle AGE$ is similar to $\triangle ACB$, $\triangle ABC \rightarrow \triangle AEG$ under an enlargement, centre A, scale factor -2; $\triangle AEG \rightarrow \triangle AEF$ under a stretch, stretch factor $\frac{3}{4}$; $\triangle AEF \rightarrow \triangle AEH$ under a shear (AE invariant line).

The area of $\triangle AEH = 4 \times \frac{3}{4} \times 1 \times 3 \, \text{cm}^2 = 9 \, \text{cm}^2$.

Combinations of transformations

The image of a point P under transformation A is $A(P)$. If another transformation B is now applied to the plane, the point $A(P)$ is transformed to $B[A(P)]$, written $BA(P)$.

BA means *transformation A followed by transformation B*. In general, $BA \neq AB$.

If BA is equivalent to the identity transformation I, $[I(P) = P$ for all points] then B is the *inverse* transformation of A and is written as A^{-1}.

Example: *S and M are the transformations of the plane: shear with x-axis invariant mapping* $(0, 1)$ *onto* $(2, 1)$, *and reflection in the line* $y = 1\frac{1}{2}$, *respectively. Illustrate the effects of MS and SM on the unit square OACB.*

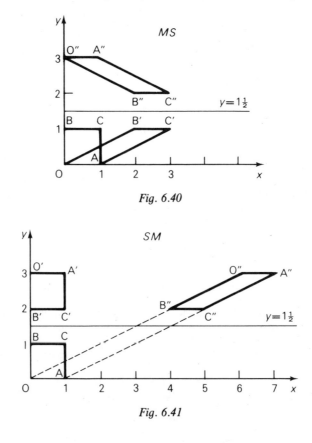

Fig. 6.40

Fig. 6.41

Figure 6.40 shows the effect of MS. The unit square OACB is first sheared onto parallelogram OAC'B', and this is then reflected in the line $y = 1\frac{1}{2}$ to parallelogram O"A"C"B". As both transformations preserve area, the area of the image is equal to the area of the square. The transformation which would map O"A"C"B" back onto OACB is M^{-1} followed by S^{-1} i.e. $(MS)^{-1} = S^{-1}M^{-1}$.

In Figure 6.41 the unit square is first reflected in the line $y = 1\frac{1}{2}$ and then sheared onto the final image $O''A''C''B''$.

Exercise 6.1

1 In a quadrilateral, three of the angles are each 77°. Calculate the fourth angle. [L]

2 Calculate an interior angle of a regular polygon with 15 sides. [L]

3 ABCD is a parallelogram with $\angle DAB = 126°$. The point E lies on BC produced so that CE = DC. Calculate $\angle CED$. [L]

4 Find the number of sides in a polygon in which the sum of the interior angles is 1080°. [JMB]

5 (a) The angles of a triangle are in the ratio 2:3:7. Calculate the largest angle.
(b) Explain very briefly why it is impossible to draw a triangle whose **sides** are in the ratio 2:3:7. [C]

6 Two angles of a quadrilateral are 90° and 150°. If the remaining two angles are $x°$ and $2x°$, calculate x. [AEB]

7 PQRS is a rhombus in which $\angle SPQ = 64°$. Equilateral triangles PXQ and QYR are drawn outside the rhombus on the sides PQ and QR. Calculate the angles of $\triangle QXY$. [L]

8 The sum of the interior angles of a polygon is less than 900°. Given that the polygon has more than four sides, find the possible numbers of sides it may have. [L]

9 ABC is a triangle and a line PQ, parallel to BC, meets AB at P and AC at Q. The line BC is produced to D and the bisector of $\angle ACD$ meets PQ produced at R. Given that $\angle QRC = 58°$ and $\angle ABC = 71°$ calculate $\angle BAC$. [JMB]

10 KLMN is a quadrilateral whose angles K, L, M, N are in the ratio of 2:3:6:7 in order. Calculate the largest and the smallest angles, and prove that KL is parallel to NM. [C]

11 $\triangle PXY$ has a fixed base XY of length 6 cm. State clearly the locus of P in two dimensions in each of the following cases:
(a) When PX = PY.
(b) When the area of $\triangle PXY = 9\,cm^2$. [L]

12 Draw the following shapes and show their axes of symmetry. (a) Rectangle, (b) Isosceles triangle. [S]

13 State which of the following quadrilaterals *must* have one or more axes of symmetry:
(a) a trapezium, (b) a rhombus, (c) a kite, (d) a parallelogram. [L]

14 A polygon of n sides is known to have $\frac{1}{2}n(n-3)$ diagonals. Find the number of sides of a polygon with 14 diagonals. [L]

15 BC is a chord of a circle, centre O. If BO is produced to meet the circle again at A and $\angle OBC = 30°$, prove that AC = OB. [L]

16 A chord of length 6 cm is drawn in a circle of radius 8 cm. Calculate the distance of the chord from the centre of the circle. [JMB]

17 A circle, centre O, touches the straight line DAF at the point A. If the points B and C lie on the circle such that $\angle DAB = 56°$ and $\angle FAC = 46°$, calculate $\angle CAB$, $\angle ABC$ and $\angle AOC$. [L]

18 (i) Calculate the length of a chord which is at a perpendicular distance of 12 cm from the centre of a circle of radius 13 cm.
(ii) The two tangents drawn from an external point T to a circle touch the circle at the points A and B respectively. If C is a point on the minor arc AB and $\angle ATB = 68°$, calculate $\angle ACB$. [L]

19 (i) Two circles of radii 8 cm and 7 cm intersect at P and Q. The tangents at P to the two circles are at right angles to each other. Calculate the distance between the two centres.

(ii) ABCDE is a pentagon in which AB = CD, BC = DE and ∠ABC = ∠CDE = 120°. Prove that the triangles ABC and CDE are congruent.

If ∠BAC = 20° and ∠BCD = 80°, find ∠BAE and prove that AB is parallel to EC. [L]

20 Two chords of a circle AB and CD intersect at X and AB is produced to a point N. Given that AX = 5 cm, XB = 7 cm, CX = 4 cm and BN = 8 cm, calculate (i) the length of DX, (ii) the length of the tangent from N to the circle, (iii) the ratio of the areas of the triangles AXC and BXC, (iv) the ratio of the areas of the triangles AXC and BXD. [AEB]

21 Describe completely the loci of points in the plane of a triangle PQR which are (i) 3 cm from P, (ii) equidistant from Q and R, (iii) equidistant from PQ and PR. [C]

22 ABCD is a cyclic quadrilateral. The diagonals AC and BD intersect at X. If ∠ADB = 39°, ∠BAC = 74° and ∠BXC = 117°, calculate ∠ABD, ∠ACD and ∠BCD. [L]

23 PQ is a diameter of a circle, centre O, radius 9 cm. The chord TS cuts PQ at R such that OR = 3 cm and TR = 8 cm. Calculate the length of TS.

If WRV is the chord of the circle perpendicular to the diameter PQ, calculate the length of WR. [L]

24

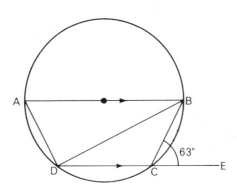

Fig. 6.42

ABCD is a cyclic quadrilateral in which AB is a diameter and DC is parallel to AB. The side DC is produced to E and ∠BCE = 63°. Calculate ∠DBC. [L]

25 (i) Calculate the third angle of a triangle in which two of the angles are 35° and 72°.

(ii) Calculate the interior angle of a regular octagon.

(iii) In a quadrilateral ABCD, ∠A = 60°, ∠B = 57° and ∠C = 123°. Calculate ∠D and state which two sides are parallel. Give a reason for your answer.

(iv) Calculate the remaining angles of a cyclic quadrilateral in which two adjacent angles are 72° and 84°. Illustrate your results in a sketch.

(v) A straight line PAB cuts a circle at A and B. If PA = 9 cm and PB = 16 cm, calculate the length of the tangent from P to the circle. [L]

Exercise 6.2 (*Transformations*)

1 A translation maps the point P(6, 3) onto the point P′(3, 5). State the coordinates of Q′, the image of Q(−1, −2) under the same translation. [JMB]

2   $\triangle_1$, $\triangle_2$, $\triangle_3$ and $\triangle_4$ are 4 triangles.
    $\triangle_2$ is the reflection of $\triangle_1$ in the line $y = x$.
    $\triangle_3$ is the clockwise rotation of $\triangle_2$ through $90°$ about the point $(1, 1)$.
    $\triangle_4$ is the enlargement of $\triangle_3$, centre the origin, with scale factor 2.
    Given that the area of $\triangle_1$ is 7 square units, calculate the area of $\triangle_4$.   [C]
3   The operation T is a translation of $+3$ units parallel to the y-axis; the operation
    M is a reflection in the line $y = x$.
        Given that A is the point $(1, 3)$, write down the coordinates of the image of A
    under the following transformations:
    (i) T^2,   (ii) M^2,   (iii) MT.   [C]
4   On graph paper, with a scale of 2 cm to 1 unit on each axis, and with axes so
    placed that x and y can each range from 0 to 7, draw the triangle T whose
    vertices are $(4, 1)$, $(4, 3)$ and $(5, 3)$.
        If Q denotes reflection in the line $x = 3$, draw $Q(T)$, i.e. the image of T under
    Q.
        If R denotes rotation of $90°$ (anticlockwise) with centre $(3, 3)$, draw $R(T)$.
    Describe in detail
    (a) a transformation P such that $PQ = R$,
    (b) a transformation S such that the vertices of $S(T)$ are $(6, 2)$, $(6, 4)$ and $(7, 4)$,
    (c) the transformation that maps $S(T)$ onto $R(T)$.   [L]
5   Given that O is the point $(0, 0)$, A is $(3, 0)$, B is $(0, 4)$, C is $(5, 5)$ and that A′, B′
    and C′ are the images of A, B and C respectively under the enlargement with
    scale factor 3 and centre O, find (i) the length A′B′, (ii) the ratio of the areas of
    the triangles ABC and A′B′C′.   [JMB]
6   The vertices of a triangle ABC have coordinates A$(0, 0)$, B $(3, 0)$ and C $(0, 4)$.
    Under a rotation the triangle is mapped onto the triangle A′B′C′ whose vertices
    have coordinates A′$(9, 0)$, B′$(9, 3)$ and C′$(5, 0)$. Using graph paper plot these
    points and draw the triangles. Construct R the centre of rotation, and describe
    clearly your construction.
        Prove that $A\hat{R}A' = 90°$ and that the y-coordinate of R is $4\frac{1}{2}$.   [C]
7   (a) Using a scale of 1 cm to each unit, draw axes and label the x-axis from 0 to
    $+18$, and the y-axis from -10 to $+12$. Plot the points A$(1, 0)$, B$(3, 2)$, C$(2, 3)$.
    (b) Construct the image of $\triangle$ABC under an enlargement, scale factor $+3$,
    centre the origin. Label the image A′B′C′.
    (c) Given that the point K $\equiv (7, 3)$, construct the image of $\triangle$A′B′C′ under an
    enlargement, scale-factor -2, centre K. Label the image A″B″C″.
    (d) Describe fully the transformation which will map $\triangle$A″B″C″ onto $\triangle$ABC,
    showing any necessary construction lines, and labelling any necessary points on
    your drawing.   [L]
8   The vertices P, Q, R and S of the square PQRS are at $(3, 5)$, $(3, 3)$, $(1, 3)$ and $(1, 5)$
    respectively. The square PQRS is rotated through $180°$ about the point $(0, 2)$.
    Find the coordinates of the vertices of the image square.
        Show that the same image square (i.e. a square with the same vertices) is
    obtained by a certain rotation about $(2, 0)$. Describe this transformation
    completely and give the coordinates of the image of P. Describe two other
    transformations of PQRS which also produce the same image square, and in
    each case give the coordinates of the image of P.   [L]

Exercise 6.3 (*Constructions*)

Use ruler and compasses only

1   Construct a triangle PQR in which PQ = 8 cm, QR = 9·7 cm and $\angle$PQR
    $= 60°$. By constructing suitable loci, find and mark clearly all the points which
    are 5 cm from P and also 5 cm from the line QR. Measure and write down the

distances of these points from Q. (All construction lines and loci must be clearly shown.) [L]

2 Draw an angle AOB of 60°.

(a) Bisect this angle and mark a point C on the bisector 7·5 cm from O.

(b) Construct a circle, centre C, which touches both OA and OB. [L]

3 Construct the triangle PQR in which PQ = 8 cm, QR = 8·5 cm and RP = 5 cm. Construct the bisector PX of the angle QPR and find the point Y on PX such that ∠YRP = 90°. Measure the lengths of YR and PY. [L]

4 Draw a straight line AB and on it mark a point X. By a geometrical construction, showing clearly all construction lines, find and mark all points which are 4 cm from X and 3 cm from the line AB. [L]

5 Construct the triangle ABC, given that AB = 6 cm, BC = 8 cm and CA = 7 cm. Construct the circle centre A, radius 3·2 cm, and also construct the tangents from C to this circle.

Construct two points P and Q, one on each tangent, which are equidistant from AB and BC. [JMB]

6 Construct in a single diagram

(i) the triangle PQR in which PQ = 12 cm, $R\hat{P}Q = 60°$ and $P\hat{Q}R = 45°$,

(ii) the point S on QR equidistant from PQ and PR,

(iii) the circle, centre S, which touches PQ.

Measure and write down the radius of this circle. [C]

7 Construct the triangle ABC with ∠ BAC = 90°, AB = 7 cm and BC = 10 cm. Find by construction the point O where the bisector of the angle ABC and the perpendicular bisector of BC meet. Measure the length of OA.

From O construct the line perpendicular to AB to meet AB at L. Measure the length of BL. [L]

8 Construct a △XYZ in which XY = 7 cm, YZ = 8 cm and ZX = 9 cm. Construct

(a) the circle which touches internally all three sides of △XYZ,

(b) the points A and B which lie on this circle and are 5 cm from Y. [L]

Section 7
Matrices and their application
to plane transformations

A matrix is a rectangular array of elements. If a matrix has m rows and n columns it is said to have **order** $m \times n$.

The number of people admitted to a swimming baths in two particular sessions may be recorded by the 2×3 matrix

	Adult swimmers	Child swimmers	Spectators
Session I	$\begin{pmatrix} 12$	40	5
Session II	26	24	$13 \end{pmatrix}$

If the charges for swimmers are $50\,p$ and $20\,p$ respectively, and for spectators $15\,p$, the 3×1 cost matrix $\begin{pmatrix} 50 \\ 20 \\ 15 \end{pmatrix}$ can be combined with the 'admissions' matrix to form the 2×1 'total takings' matrix:

$$\begin{pmatrix} 12 & 40 & 5 \\ 26 & 24 & 13 \end{pmatrix} \begin{pmatrix} 50 \\ 20 \\ 15 \end{pmatrix} = \begin{pmatrix} 12 \times 50 + 40 \times 20 + 5 \times 15 \\ 26 \times 50 + 24 \times 20 + 13 \times 15 \end{pmatrix} = \begin{pmatrix} 1475 \\ 1975 \end{pmatrix}.$$

This illustrates the use of the rule for multiplying matrices defined below.

Algebra of matrices

Addition

Only matrices of the same order can be added, the elements of the resulting matrix being formed by adding corresponding elements.

Example: $\begin{pmatrix} 1 & 2 \\ 3 & 4 \end{pmatrix} + \begin{pmatrix} 5 & -6 \\ -7 & 8 \end{pmatrix} = \begin{pmatrix} 6 & -4 \\ -4 & 12 \end{pmatrix}.$

Null matrix

The matrix $\begin{pmatrix} 0 & 0 \\ 0 & 0 \end{pmatrix}$ is called the zero or null matrix and is usually denoted by $\mathbf{O}$. It is the identity element under addition.

Matrices are both (a) commutative and (b) associative under addition, for if **A**, **B** and **C** are matrices of the same order

$$\text{(a)} \quad \mathbf{A} + \mathbf{B} = \mathbf{B} + \mathbf{A}, \quad \text{(b)} \quad (\mathbf{A} + \mathbf{B}) + \mathbf{C} = \mathbf{A} + (\mathbf{B} + \mathbf{C}).$$

Equality

Two matrices are equal if, and only if, they are of the same order and corresponding elements are equal.

$$\begin{pmatrix} x & 3 \\ 4 & y \end{pmatrix} = \begin{pmatrix} 1 & a \\ b & 6 \end{pmatrix} \Leftrightarrow x = 1, a = 3, b = 4, y = 6.$$

Multiplication of a matrix by a number

A matrix **A**, multiplied by a number k, is equivalent to the matrix whose elements are each k times those of **A**, e.g.

$$3\begin{pmatrix} 4 & -1 \\ 7 & 8 \end{pmatrix} = \begin{pmatrix} 12 & -3 \\ 21 & 24 \end{pmatrix}.$$

Example: *Given that* $m\begin{pmatrix} 3 \\ 4 \end{pmatrix} - 5\begin{pmatrix} 2 \\ n \end{pmatrix} = \begin{pmatrix} 2 \\ 1 \end{pmatrix}$, *find m and n.*

$$m\begin{pmatrix} 3 \\ 4 \end{pmatrix} - 5\begin{pmatrix} 2 \\ n \end{pmatrix} = \begin{pmatrix} 3m \\ 4m \end{pmatrix} - \begin{pmatrix} 10 \\ 5n \end{pmatrix} = \begin{pmatrix} 3m - 10 \\ 4m - 5n \end{pmatrix}$$

$$\begin{pmatrix} 3m - 10 \\ 4m - 5n \end{pmatrix} = \begin{pmatrix} 2 \\ 1 \end{pmatrix} \Rightarrow \begin{matrix} 3m - 10 = 2 \\ 4m - 5n = 1 \end{matrix} \Rightarrow m = 4, n = 3.$$

Multiplication of two matrices

If a matrix **A** has order $m \times n$ and a matrix **B** has order $p \times q$, the product **AB** is only possible if $n = p$, the product matrix being of order $m \times q$. The elements of the product matrix are found by combining *rows* of **A** with *columns* of **B** in the following manner:

$$\overset{\mathbf{A}}{\begin{pmatrix} a & b \\ c & d \end{pmatrix}} \overset{\mathbf{B}}{\begin{pmatrix} e & f & g \\ h & i & j \end{pmatrix}} = \overset{\mathbf{AB}}{\begin{pmatrix} ae + bh & af + bi & ag + bj \\ ce + dh & cf + di & cg + dj \end{pmatrix}}$$

Order $\qquad 2 \times 2 \qquad 2 \times 3 \qquad\qquad\qquad 2 \times 3$

If row 2, say, of **A**, and column 3, say, of **B** are chosen, the result of summing the separate products of corresponding elements (i.e. 1st with 1st, 2nd with 2nd, etc.) is the element in row 2, column 3 of the product matrix.

To form the product **AB**, **B** is pre-multiplied by **A**, or **A** is post-multiplied by **B**.

Example: (a) $\begin{pmatrix} 5 & 6 \\ 9 & 4 \end{pmatrix}\begin{pmatrix} 4 & 6 \\ -1 & 0 \end{pmatrix} = \begin{pmatrix} 5\times4+6\times(-1) & 5\times6+6\times0 \\ 9\times4+4\times(-1) & 9\times6+4\times0 \end{pmatrix}$

$$= \begin{pmatrix} 14 & 30 \\ 32 & 54 \end{pmatrix}.$$

(b) $\begin{pmatrix} 4 & 6 \\ -1 & 0 \end{pmatrix}\begin{pmatrix} 5 & 6 \\ 9 & 4 \end{pmatrix} = \begin{pmatrix} 4\times5+6\times9 & 4\times6+6\times4 \\ (-1)\times5+0\times9 & (-1)\times6+0\times4 \end{pmatrix}$

$$= \begin{pmatrix} 74 & 48 \\ -5 & -6 \end{pmatrix}.$$

This example illustrates the fact that, in general, matrices are **not commutative** under multiplication, i.e. $\mathbf{AB} \neq \mathbf{BA}$.

In many cases the product cannot be formed in the reverse order, as with the admissions matrix and cost matrix given earlier.

Matrices are **associative** under multiplication i.e. $\mathbf{A}(\mathbf{BC}) = (\mathbf{AB})\mathbf{C}$.

Example: *Given that* $\mathbf{A} = \begin{pmatrix} 4 & 0 \\ -1 & 2 \end{pmatrix}$ *and* $\mathbf{B} = \begin{pmatrix} 3 & 2 \\ 1 & -4 \end{pmatrix}$ *find*

(a) $\mathbf{A} + \mathbf{B}$, (b) $\mathbf{A} - \mathbf{B}$, (c) $\mathbf{A}^2$, (d) $\mathbf{B}^2$, (e) $\mathbf{A}^2 - \mathbf{B}^2$,

(f) $(\mathbf{A} + \mathbf{B})(\mathbf{A} - \mathbf{B})$.

(a) $\mathbf{A} + \mathbf{B} = \begin{pmatrix} 7 & 2 \\ 0 & -2 \end{pmatrix}$, (b) $\mathbf{A} - \mathbf{B} = \begin{pmatrix} 1 & -2 \\ -2 & 6 \end{pmatrix}$,

(c) $\mathbf{A}^2 = \begin{pmatrix} 4 & 0 \\ -1 & 2 \end{pmatrix}\begin{pmatrix} 4 & 0 \\ -1 & 2 \end{pmatrix} = \begin{pmatrix} 16 & 0 \\ -6 & 4 \end{pmatrix}$,

(d) $\mathbf{B}^2 = \begin{pmatrix} 3 & 2 \\ 1 & -4 \end{pmatrix}\begin{pmatrix} 3 & 2 \\ 1 & -4 \end{pmatrix} = \begin{pmatrix} 11 & -2 \\ -1 & 18 \end{pmatrix}$,

(e) $\mathbf{A}^2 - \mathbf{B}^2 = \begin{pmatrix} 5 & 2 \\ -5 & -14 \end{pmatrix}$,

(f) $(\mathbf{A} + \mathbf{B})(\mathbf{A} - \mathbf{B}) = \begin{pmatrix} 7 & 2 \\ 0 & -2 \end{pmatrix}\begin{pmatrix} 1 & -2 \\ -2 & 6 \end{pmatrix} = \begin{pmatrix} 3 & -2 \\ 4 & -12 \end{pmatrix}$.

Note that $\mathbf{A}^2 - \mathbf{B}^2 \neq (\mathbf{A} + \mathbf{B})(\mathbf{A} - \mathbf{B})$.

Unit matrix

The matrix $\mathbf{I} = \begin{pmatrix} 1 & 0 \\ 0 & 1 \end{pmatrix}$ is called the unit matrix of order 2; unit matrices have 1's along the leading diagonal, 0's in all other positions.

The unit matrix is the identity matrix under multiplication, and commutes with all matrices of the same order.

Determinant of a matrix

For the matrix $A = \begin{pmatrix} a & b \\ c & d \end{pmatrix}$ the quantity $ad - bc$ is called the **determinant** of **A**.

If the determinant is zero, the matrix is said to be **singular**.

Example: (a) The determinant of $\begin{pmatrix} 3 & -6 \\ 2 & 5 \end{pmatrix}$ is $(3 \times 5) - (2 \times -6)$
$$= 15 + 12 = 27.$$

(b) The matrix $\begin{pmatrix} 3 & 6 \\ 2 & 4 \end{pmatrix}$ is singular since $(3 \times 4) - (2 \times 6) = 0$.

Inverse of a matrix

If **B** is a matrix such that $AB = BA = I$ then **B** is called the inverse of **A** and is denoted by A^{-1}.

For the matrix $A = \begin{pmatrix} a & b \\ c & d \end{pmatrix}$ it can be shown that

$$A^{-1} = \frac{1}{ad - bc} \begin{pmatrix} d & -b \\ -c & a \end{pmatrix} = \begin{pmatrix} \dfrac{d}{ad-bc} & \dfrac{-b}{ad-bc} \\ \dfrac{-c}{ad-bc} & \dfrac{a}{ad-bc} \end{pmatrix}$$

providing that $ad - bc \neq 0$. A singular matrix has no inverse.

Example: The matrix $A = \begin{pmatrix} 3 & 4 \\ 1 & 2 \end{pmatrix}$ has determinant $= (3 \times 2) - (4 \times 1)$
$$= 2.$$
The inverse of $A = \dfrac{1}{2} \begin{pmatrix} 2 & -4 \\ -1 & 3 \end{pmatrix} = \begin{pmatrix} 1 & -2 \\ -\frac{1}{2} & 1\frac{1}{2} \end{pmatrix}$

Note that for the equation $AB = AC$, where **A** is not singular or the zero matrix, pre-multiplying by A^{-1} gives the result $B = C$. But if **A** is singular **B** need not equal **C**.

Example: Let $A = \begin{pmatrix} 3 & 6 \\ 2 & 4 \end{pmatrix}$ and $B = \begin{pmatrix} 1 & -5 \\ 6 & 2 \end{pmatrix}$, then $AB = \begin{pmatrix} 39 & -3 \\ 26 & -2 \end{pmatrix}$.

There are an infinite number of matrices **C** such that $AC = \begin{pmatrix} 39 & -3 \\ 26 & -2 \end{pmatrix}$.

$\begin{pmatrix} 3 & 6 \\ 2 & 4 \end{pmatrix} \begin{pmatrix} a & b \\ c & d \end{pmatrix} = \begin{pmatrix} 39 & -3 \\ 26 & -2 \end{pmatrix} \Rightarrow 2a + 4c = 26$ and $2b + 4d = -2$,
$$\Rightarrow a + 2c = 13 \text{ and } b + 2d = -1.$$

One possibility for **C** is $\begin{pmatrix} 5 & 1 \\ 4 & -1 \end{pmatrix}$.

Transpose of a matrix

If the rows and columns of a matrix are interchanged the transpose is formed.

The transpose of $\mathbf{A} = \begin{pmatrix} 1 & 2 & 3 \\ 4 & 5 & 6 \end{pmatrix}$ is $\mathbf{A}^T = \begin{pmatrix} 1 & 4 \\ 2 & 5 \\ 3 & 6 \end{pmatrix}$.

Example: *The matrix* $\mathbf{A} = \begin{pmatrix} 3 & 4 \\ x & 2 \end{pmatrix}$ *is such that* $\mathbf{AA}^T = \begin{pmatrix} 25 & 11 \\ 11 & y \end{pmatrix}$.
Find x and y.

$$\mathbf{A}^T = \begin{pmatrix} 3 & x \\ 4 & 2 \end{pmatrix} \Rightarrow \mathbf{AA}^T = \begin{pmatrix} 3 & 4 \\ x & 2 \end{pmatrix}\begin{pmatrix} 3 & x \\ 4 & 2 \end{pmatrix} = \begin{pmatrix} 25 & 3x+8 \\ 3x+8 & x^2+4 \end{pmatrix},$$

$$\begin{pmatrix} 25 & 3x+8 \\ 3x+8 & x^2+4 \end{pmatrix} = \begin{pmatrix} 25 & 11 \\ 11 & y \end{pmatrix} \Rightarrow x = 1, \ y = 5.$$

Matrix representations of transformations of the plane

If a point (x, y) is written as the 2×1 matrix $\begin{pmatrix} x \\ y \end{pmatrix}$ the position vector of the point, and $\mathbf{A}$ is a 2×2 matrix, the product $\mathbf{A}\begin{pmatrix} x \\ y \end{pmatrix}$ forms a 2×1 matrix $\begin{pmatrix} x' \\ y' \end{pmatrix}$, say. All points of the plane can be transformed in this way and $\mathbf{A}$, therefore, can be interpreted as a transformation of the plane mapping (x, y) on to its image (x', y').

Let
$$\mathbf{A} = \begin{pmatrix} a & b \\ c & d \end{pmatrix}.$$

As
$$\begin{pmatrix} a & b \\ c & d \end{pmatrix}\begin{pmatrix} 0 \\ 0 \end{pmatrix} = \begin{pmatrix} 0 \\ 0 \end{pmatrix}, \qquad \begin{pmatrix} a & b \\ c & d \end{pmatrix}\begin{pmatrix} 1 \\ 0 \end{pmatrix} = \begin{pmatrix} a \\ c \end{pmatrix},$$

$$\begin{pmatrix} a & b \\ c & d \end{pmatrix}\begin{pmatrix} 0 \\ 1 \end{pmatrix} = \begin{pmatrix} b \\ d \end{pmatrix}, \qquad \begin{pmatrix} a & b \\ c & d \end{pmatrix}\begin{pmatrix} 1 \\ 1 \end{pmatrix} = \begin{pmatrix} a+b \\ c+d \end{pmatrix},$$

we may deduce that:
(a) only transformations for which the origin is an invariant point can be represented by 2×2 matrices,
(b) if $(1, 0) \rightarrow (a, c)$ under a transformation then $\begin{pmatrix} a \\ c \end{pmatrix}$ is the first column of its matrix,
(c) if $(0, 1) \rightarrow (b, d)$ under a transformation then $\begin{pmatrix} b \\ d \end{pmatrix}$ is the second column of its matrix,
(d) $(1, 1) \rightarrow (a+b, c+d)$.

If the images of (1, 0) *and* (0, 1) *are known the matrix of the transformation can be readily found.*

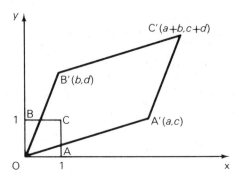

Fig. 7.1

Figure 7.1 shows the image OA'C'B' of the unit square OACB under the transformation represented by $\mathbf{A} = \begin{pmatrix} a & b \\ c & d \end{pmatrix}$. In general, squares become parallelograms, the values a, b, c, d determining the nature of the parallelogram. In the case of a non-zero singular matrix the image becomes a straight line.

The area of parallelogram OA'C'B' can be shown to be $ad - bc$, the value of the determinant of matrix $\mathbf{A}$. The determinant indicates the area scale factor involved in the transformation, any minus sign indicating a 'turning over' of the plane, as in a reflection, for example.

Example: *For the transformation in which all points on the x-axis are invariant and* (0, 1) → ($\frac{1}{2}$, 1), *show on a diagram the image of the triangle whose vertices are* (0, 2), (0, 3) *and* (1, 3).

As (1, 0) → (1, 0) and (0, 1) → ($\frac{1}{2}$, 1), the matrix of the transformation is $\begin{pmatrix} 1 & \frac{1}{2} \\ 0 & 1 \end{pmatrix}$.

As $\begin{pmatrix} 1 & \frac{1}{2} \\ 0 & 1 \end{pmatrix}\begin{pmatrix} 0 & 0 & 1 \\ 2 & 3 & 3 \end{pmatrix} = \begin{pmatrix} 1 & 1\frac{1}{2} & 2\frac{1}{2} \\ 2 & 3 & 3 \end{pmatrix}$,

(0, 2) → (1, 2), (0, 3) → (1$\frac{1}{2}$, 3) and (1, 3) → (2$\frac{1}{2}$, 3).

Figure 7.2 shows the given triangle PQR and its image triangle P'Q'R'. The axis Oy is mapped onto OY and all lines parallel to Oy are mapped onto lines parallel to OY as shown.

The image of the unit square indicates the general picture for the plane.

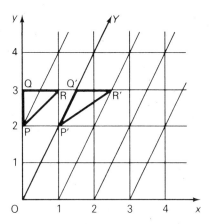

Fig. 7.2

Reflections in the following lines through the origin

The matrices representing the following transformations should be verified by finding the images of $(1, 0)$ and $(0, 1)$ in each case.

(a) line $x = 0$ (y-axis),   (b) line $y = 0$ (x-axis),   (c) line $y = x$,   (d) line $y = -x$,

$$\begin{pmatrix} -1 & 0 \\ 0 & 1 \end{pmatrix} \qquad \begin{pmatrix} 1 & 0 \\ 0 & -1 \end{pmatrix} \qquad \begin{pmatrix} 0 & 1 \\ 1 & 0 \end{pmatrix} \qquad \begin{pmatrix} 0 & -1 \\ -1 & 0 \end{pmatrix}$$

Rotations about the origin through an angle of

(a) 90° anti-clockwise $(+90°)$,   (b) 90° clock-wise $(-90°)$,   (c) 180° (half turn),   (d) 360° (full turn).

$$\begin{pmatrix} 0 & -1 \\ 1 & 0 \end{pmatrix} \qquad \begin{pmatrix} 0 & 1 \\ -1 & 0 \end{pmatrix} \qquad \begin{pmatrix} -1 & 0 \\ 0 & -1 \end{pmatrix} \qquad \begin{pmatrix} 1 & 0 \\ 0 & 1 \end{pmatrix}$$

The transformation represented by the unit matrix **I** is called the identity transformation since all points remain invariant.

Enlargement, centre the origin, scale factor k

As $(1, 0) \rightarrow (k, 0)$ and $(0, 1) \rightarrow (0, k)$ the matrix is $\begin{pmatrix} k & 0 \\ 0 & k \end{pmatrix}$.

If $0 < k < 1$, all points P have images on OP nearer to the origin;
if $k < 0$, all points P have images on PO produced.

Shear, with either the x-axis or y-axis invariant

(a) *x-axis invariant*

As $(1, 0)$ is invariant and $(0, 1)$ moves parallel to Ox the matrix is $\begin{pmatrix} 1 & k \\ 0 & 1 \end{pmatrix}$.

If $k > 0$, the half plane $y > 0$ moves to the right, the half plane $y < 0$ moves to the left in the shearing, and vice versa if $k < 0$.

75

(b) *y-axis invariant*

As $(0, 1)$ is invariant and $(1, 0)$ moves parallel to Oy the matrix is $\begin{pmatrix} 1 & 0 \\ k & 1 \end{pmatrix}$.

If $k > 0$, the half plane $x > 0$ moves up, the half plane $x < 0$ moves down in the shearing, and vice versa if $k < 0$.

Figure 7.2 shows the effect of the shear $\begin{pmatrix} 1 & \frac{1}{2} \\ 0 & 1 \end{pmatrix}$ on the plane and, in particular, $\triangle$PQR.

Stretch, with either the x-axis or y-axis invariant

(a) *x-axis invariant*

As $(1, 0)$ is invariant and $(0, 1)$ moves parallel to Oy the matrix is $\begin{pmatrix} 1 & 0 \\ 0 & k \end{pmatrix}$.

(b) *y-axis invariant*

As $(0, 1)$ is invariant and $(1, 0)$ moves parallel to Ox the matrix is $\begin{pmatrix} k & 0 \\ 0 & 1 \end{pmatrix}$.

Example: *In Figure 7.3 a shearing of the plane maps $\triangle ABC$ on to $\triangle ABC'$. Find the matrix of the shear and the image of the point $(-1, 2)$.*

As the shear has y-axis invariant the matrix is of the form $\begin{pmatrix} 1 & 0 \\ k & 1 \end{pmatrix}$.

$$(2, 3) \to (2, 0) \Rightarrow \begin{pmatrix} 1 & 0 \\ k & 1 \end{pmatrix}\begin{pmatrix} 2 \\ 3 \end{pmatrix} = \begin{pmatrix} 2 \\ 0 \end{pmatrix} \Rightarrow 2k + 3 = 0 \Rightarrow k = -1\tfrac{1}{2}.$$

The matrix of the shear is $\begin{pmatrix} 1 & 0 \\ -1\frac{1}{2} & 1 \end{pmatrix}$.

As $\begin{pmatrix} 1 & 0 \\ -1\frac{1}{2} & 1 \end{pmatrix}\begin{pmatrix} -1 \\ 2 \end{pmatrix} = \begin{pmatrix} -1 \\ 3\frac{1}{2} \end{pmatrix}$, the image of $(-1, 2)$ is $(-1, 3\tfrac{1}{2})$.

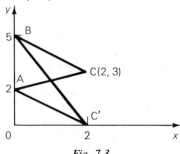

Fig. 7.3

Combinations of transformations

Figure 7.4 shows the effect on the unit square of first shearing with the x-axis invariant and $(0, 1) \to (2, 1)$, and then reflecting in the y-axis. As $(1, 0) \to (-1, 0)$ and $(0, 1) \to (-2, 1)$ the matrix representing the single

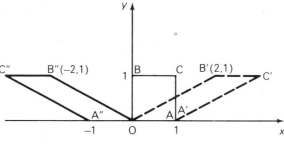

Fig. 7.4

transformation equivalent to first shearing and then reflecting is $\begin{pmatrix} -1 & -2 \\ 0 & 1 \end{pmatrix}$.

The matrix of the shear is $\begin{pmatrix} 1 & 2 \\ 0 & 1 \end{pmatrix}$ and the matrix of the reflection is $\begin{pmatrix} -1 & 0 \\ 0 & 1 \end{pmatrix}$. We see that the matrix product

$$\begin{pmatrix} -1 & 0 \\ 0 & 1 \end{pmatrix}\begin{pmatrix} 1 & 2 \\ 0 & 1 \end{pmatrix} = \begin{pmatrix} -1 & -2 \\ 0 & 1 \end{pmatrix}.$$

If the matrices are multiplied in the reverse order the result would represent the single transformation equivalent to the reflection followed by the shear.

In general, if **A** is the matrix associated with transformation X and **B** is the matrix associated with transformation Y, the matrix product **AB** represents the single transformation equivalent to 'Y followed by X'.

Example: *Find the matrix of the single transformation equivalent to a rotation through $90°$ anticlockwise about O followed by a stretch with y-axis invariant, $(1, 0) \rightarrow (3, 0)$.*

$\mathbf{R} = \begin{pmatrix} 0 & -1 \\ 1 & 0 \end{pmatrix}$ represents the rotation, $\mathbf{U} = \begin{pmatrix} 3 & 0 \\ 0 & 1 \end{pmatrix}$ represents the stretch.
The matrix for 'rotation followed by stretch' is

$$\mathbf{UR} = \begin{pmatrix} 3 & 0 \\ 0 & 1 \end{pmatrix}\begin{pmatrix} 0 & -1 \\ 1 & 0 \end{pmatrix} = \begin{pmatrix} 0 & -3 \\ 1 & 0 \end{pmatrix}.$$

Example: *If X is the matrix representing a reflection in the x-axis and S represents the shear, y-axis invariant, mapping $(1, 0)$ to $(1, 4)$, find (a) S^5, (b) the images of the points $(1, 2)$, $(3, -1)$ and $(5, 6)$ after the reflection followed by the shear, (c) the matrix of the transformation which maps the images of these points back onto $(1, 2)$, $(3, -1)$ and $(5, 6)$ respectively.*

(a) $\mathbf{S}^5$ represents the shear carried out 5 times in succession.
As $(1, 0) \rightarrow (1, 20)$ and $(0, 1) \rightarrow (0, 1)$, the matrix is $\begin{pmatrix} 1 & 0 \\ 20 & 1 \end{pmatrix}$.

(b) The matrix of 'the reflection followed by the shear' is

$$SX = \begin{pmatrix} 1 & 0 \\ 4 & 1 \end{pmatrix}\begin{pmatrix} 1 & 0 \\ 0 & -1 \end{pmatrix} = \begin{pmatrix} 1 & 0 \\ 4 & -1 \end{pmatrix}.$$

As

$$\begin{pmatrix} 1 & 0 \\ 4 & -1 \end{pmatrix}\begin{pmatrix} 1 & 3 & 5 \\ 2 & -1 & 6 \end{pmatrix} = \begin{pmatrix} 1 & 3 & 5 \\ 2 & 13 & 14 \end{pmatrix},$$

$(1, 2) \rightarrow (1, 2)$, $(3, -1) \rightarrow (3, 13)$, $(5, 6) \rightarrow (5, 14)$.

(c) The inverse transformation, represented by the inverse matrix, will map all images back onto their object points.

The inverse of $\begin{pmatrix} 1 & 0 \\ 4 & -1 \end{pmatrix}$ is $\begin{pmatrix} 1 & 0 \\ 4 & -1 \end{pmatrix}$; it is a self-inverse matrix.

Exercise 7.1

1 $A = \begin{pmatrix} 1 & 1 \\ 0 & 2 \end{pmatrix}$, $B = \begin{pmatrix} 3 & 4 \\ 0 & 5 \end{pmatrix}$.
   (a) Express as a single matrix
   (i) $A + B$, (ii) AB, (iii) BA.
   (b) Write down the inverse of A.   [CA]

2 Find the value of
   (a) $\begin{pmatrix} 5 & 2 \\ 2 & 6 \end{pmatrix} + \begin{pmatrix} 5 & -2 \\ 2 & 1 \end{pmatrix}$, (b) $(1 \ \ 3)\begin{pmatrix} 2 & -1 \\ 0 & 3 \end{pmatrix}$.   [S]

3 (i) Find the matrix product $\begin{pmatrix} 1 & -3 \\ -2 & 8 \end{pmatrix}\begin{pmatrix} 8 & 3 \\ 2 & 1 \end{pmatrix}$.
   (ii) Solve the simultaneous equations $8x + 3y = 7$,
   $\qquad\qquad\qquad\qquad\qquad\qquad\qquad 2x + y = 2$.   [C]

4 Find x and y given that
   $$\begin{pmatrix} x \\ y \end{pmatrix} = \begin{pmatrix} 3 & 2 \\ 0 & 1 \end{pmatrix}\begin{pmatrix} 2 \\ 1 \end{pmatrix} + \begin{pmatrix} 2 \\ -1 \end{pmatrix}.$$ [AEB]

5 Given that the matrices A and B are such that
   $$3A = \begin{pmatrix} 1 & 0 \\ 2 & 3 \end{pmatrix}\begin{pmatrix} 3 & 3 \\ -1 & 0 \end{pmatrix} \text{ and that } \begin{pmatrix} 1 & 2 \\ 3 & 8 \end{pmatrix}B = \begin{pmatrix} 1 & 0 \\ 0 & 1 \end{pmatrix},$$
   find A and B.   [C]

6 Write down and simplify the determinant of $\begin{pmatrix} c & 3 \\ 4 & c+4 \end{pmatrix}$.
   Hence find two values of c for which the matrix is singular.   [L]

7 Find A^{-1}, the inverse of the matrix $A = \begin{pmatrix} 4 & 6 \\ 5 & 8 \end{pmatrix}$.   [M]

8 Find a and b in the matrix multiplication, $\begin{pmatrix} 5 & 1 \\ 3 & 2 \end{pmatrix}\begin{pmatrix} a \\ 2 \end{pmatrix} = \begin{pmatrix} 12 \\ b \end{pmatrix}$.   [M]

9 Describe completely the geometrical transformation associated with the matrix
   $\begin{pmatrix} -1 & 0 \\ 0 & 1 \end{pmatrix}$.   [JMB]

10 State what transformation is associated with each of the matrices
   $$M = \begin{pmatrix} 0 & -1 \\ 1 & 0 \end{pmatrix} \text{ and } N = \begin{pmatrix} 2 & 0 \\ 0 & 2 \end{pmatrix}.$$

If $P = \begin{pmatrix} 1 & -1 \\ 1 & 1 \end{pmatrix}$, show that $P^2 = MN$, and hence, or otherwise, find what transformation is associated with P. [L]

11 A transformation T is defined by
$$T : \begin{pmatrix} x \\ y \end{pmatrix} \rightarrow \begin{pmatrix} 0 & 1 \\ -1 & 0 \end{pmatrix} \begin{pmatrix} x \\ y \end{pmatrix} + \begin{pmatrix} 3 \\ 1 \end{pmatrix}.$$
P is the point (p, q) which is mapped onto itself under the transformation. Calculate the values of p and q. [CA]

12 Given that $A = \begin{pmatrix} 3 & 1 \\ 5 & -2 \end{pmatrix}$, $B = \begin{pmatrix} 2 & 0 \\ 1 & -1 \end{pmatrix}$ and $x = \begin{pmatrix} 1 \\ 2 \end{pmatrix}$, find the elements of the following column vectors
(a) $Ax + Bx$,   (b) ABx. [L]

13 (a) Evaluate $2 \begin{pmatrix} 1 & 2 \\ 3 & 4 \end{pmatrix} - \begin{pmatrix} 2 & 3 \\ 5 & 7 \end{pmatrix}$.

(b) Find x given that $(2x \quad 3) \begin{pmatrix} 11 \\ -6x \end{pmatrix} = (100)$. [C]

14 Draw a network which can be represented by the route matrix
To
$$\begin{array}{c} \\ \text{From} \end{array} \begin{array}{c} \\ A \\ B \end{array} \begin{pmatrix} 2 & 1 \\ 1 & 0 \end{pmatrix}.$$
(with column labels $A \quad B$) [CA]

15 A linear transformation from $\mathbb{R}^2$ to $\mathbb{R}^2$ is defined by $p = Mq$, where M is a 2×2 matrix and p and q are 2×1 column vectors. Given that $p = \begin{pmatrix} 1 \\ 4 \end{pmatrix}$ when $q = \begin{pmatrix} 1 \\ 0 \end{pmatrix}$ and $p = \begin{pmatrix} -3 \\ 3 \end{pmatrix}$ when $q = \begin{pmatrix} -1 \\ 1 \end{pmatrix}$, find M. [L]

16 Find the values of x and y such that $\begin{pmatrix} 5 & 2 \\ 7 & 3 \end{pmatrix} \begin{pmatrix} x \\ y \end{pmatrix} = \begin{pmatrix} 1 \\ 2 \end{pmatrix}$. [JMB]

17 Evaluate the matrix product $\begin{pmatrix} 2 & 3 \\ -1 & \frac{1}{2} \end{pmatrix} \begin{pmatrix} 4 & \frac{1}{4} \\ 2 & \frac{1}{2} \end{pmatrix}$. [C]

18 Given that M is the matrix $\begin{pmatrix} 0 \cdot 6 & 0 \cdot 8 \\ 0 \cdot 8 & -0 \cdot 6 \end{pmatrix}$, calculate the matrix product
$$M \begin{pmatrix} 10 & 10 & 0 \\ 0 & 5 & 5 \end{pmatrix},$$
and hence write down the coordinates of the images A', B', C' of the points $A(10, 0)$, $B(10, 5)$, $C(0, 5)$ under the transformation whose matrix is M. [L]

19 Form the product $(a \quad b) \begin{pmatrix} c \\ d \end{pmatrix}$, and find the value of d in order that the product may be a zero matrix if $a = 3$, $b = 2$, and $c = -5$.

Form the 2×2 matrix which is the product $\begin{pmatrix} c \\ d \end{pmatrix} (a \quad b)$, and show that this product matrix is singular for all values of a, b, c and d. [L]

20 Evaluate the matrix product $\begin{pmatrix} 2 & -1 \\ 1 & 3 \end{pmatrix} \begin{pmatrix} 3 & 1 \\ -1 & 2 \end{pmatrix}$. [JMB]

Exercise 7.2

1 Given that $A = \begin{pmatrix} 1 & 0 \\ 3 & 1 \end{pmatrix}$, $B = \begin{pmatrix} 1 & 0 \\ 5 & 1 \end{pmatrix}$, $X = \begin{pmatrix} 1 & 0 \\ x & 1 \end{pmatrix}$, $Y = \begin{pmatrix} 1 & 0 \\ y & 1 \end{pmatrix}$, find A^2, B^2, AB, XY. (You are recommended to use these results throughout the rest of this question.)

79

(a) Find the matrix product $\begin{pmatrix} 1 & 0 \\ 7 & 1 \end{pmatrix}\begin{pmatrix} 1 & 0 \\ 9 & 1 \end{pmatrix}$.

(b) Given that $\mathbf{P} = \begin{pmatrix} 1 & 0 \\ 11 & 1 \end{pmatrix}$, $\mathbf{Q} = \begin{pmatrix} 1 & 0 \\ 19 & 1 \end{pmatrix}$, express $\mathbf{P}$ and $\mathbf{Q}$ in terms of powers of $\mathbf{A}$ and $\mathbf{B}$.

(c) Find the value of k for which
$$\mathbf{B}\begin{pmatrix} 1 & 0 \\ k & 1 \end{pmatrix} = \begin{pmatrix} 1 & 0 \\ 0 & 1 \end{pmatrix}.$$

(d) If $\mathbf{AX}^2 = \mathbf{BY}$, express y in terms of x. [L]

2 It is given that $\mathbf{A} = \begin{pmatrix} 2 & 0 \\ 3 & 1 \end{pmatrix}$ and $\mathbf{B} = \begin{pmatrix} 1 & x \\ y & -1 \end{pmatrix}$.

(i) Find the matrix product $\mathbf{AB}$.

(ii) Given that $\mathbf{B} + p\mathbf{A} = \begin{pmatrix} 7 & 5 \\ 13 & z \end{pmatrix}$, find the values of x, y, z and p.

(iii) Evaluate the matrix product $\mathbf{A}\begin{pmatrix} k \\ 3k \end{pmatrix}$. Hence write down the equation of the straight line which is invariant under the transformation whose matrix is $\mathbf{A}$. [C]

3 It is given that $\mathbf{A} = \begin{pmatrix} 3 & 1 \\ 2 & 4 \end{pmatrix}$, $\mathbf{B} = \begin{pmatrix} 1 & -2 \\ 3 & 0 \end{pmatrix}$ and $\mathbf{C} = \begin{pmatrix} 0 & \frac{1}{3} \\ -\frac{1}{2} & \frac{1}{6} \end{pmatrix}$.

(a) Find $\mathbf{A} + \mathbf{B}$.

(b) Find $3\mathbf{A} - 2\mathbf{B}$.

(c) Find $\mathbf{A}(\mathbf{BC})$.

(d) When multiplied by a constant k, the inverse of $\mathbf{AB}$ is $\begin{pmatrix} -2 & 3 \\ -7 & 3 \end{pmatrix}$. Find k.

(e) Find the values of x and y given that $\begin{pmatrix} x & y \\ 4x & -6y \end{pmatrix}\begin{pmatrix} 2 & 1 \\ 1 & 0 \end{pmatrix} = \begin{pmatrix} 3 & 1 \\ 2 & 4 \end{pmatrix}$. [S]

4 $\mathbf{M} = \begin{pmatrix} -a & -1 \\ a^2 - a + 1 & a - 1 \end{pmatrix}$. Find the determinant of $\mathbf{M}$, and state why $\mathbf{M}$ cannot be singular.

(i) Write down the inverse, $\mathbf{M}^{-1}$, of $\mathbf{M}$.

(ii) Evaluate $\mathbf{M}^2$ and show that $\mathbf{M}^2 = \mathbf{M}^{-1}$. [L]

5 (a) $\mathbf{A}$, $\mathbf{B}$, $\mathbf{C}$ are the following 2×2 matrices
$$\mathbf{A} = \begin{pmatrix} 4 & 1 \\ 2 & 3 \end{pmatrix}, \quad \mathbf{B} = \begin{pmatrix} 1 & 2 \\ 0 & 1 \end{pmatrix}, \quad \mathbf{C} = \begin{pmatrix} 3 & 0 \\ 0 & 3 \end{pmatrix}.$$
Find (i) $\mathbf{AB}$, (ii) $\mathbf{AC}$, (iii) $\mathbf{A}(\mathbf{B} + \mathbf{C})$.

(b) $\mathbf{D}$, $\mathbf{E}$ are the following 2×2 matrices
$$\mathbf{D} = \begin{pmatrix} 3 & 1 \\ 5 & 2 \end{pmatrix}, \quad \mathbf{E} = \begin{pmatrix} 2 & -1 \\ -5 & 3 \end{pmatrix}.$$

Find (i) $\mathbf{DE}$, (ii) $\mathbf{ED}$. [M]

6 (i) $\mathbf{A} = \begin{pmatrix} -4 & 4 & 3 \\ -1 & 1 & 1 \end{pmatrix}$ and $\mathbf{B} = \begin{pmatrix} 2 & 1 \\ 3 & -2 \\ -1 & 4 \end{pmatrix}$.

(a) Find the matrix products $\mathbf{AB}$ and $\mathbf{BA}$.

(b) Hence, or otherwise, find the matrix products $\mathbf{ABA}$ and $\mathbf{BAB}$, and show that $(\mathbf{BA})^2 = \mathbf{BA}$.

(c) State whether or not $\mathbf{B}$ is the inverse of $\mathbf{A}$, giving a reason for your answer.

(ii) Given that $\begin{pmatrix} 3 & -3 \\ -4 & 5 \end{pmatrix}\begin{pmatrix} x \\ y \end{pmatrix} = \begin{pmatrix} 6 \\ 9 \end{pmatrix}$,

find x and y. [L]

7 The vertices of a triangle X have coordinates $A(-1, 8)$, $B(4, 8)$, $C(0, 5)$.

(i) Using a scale of 1 cm to represent 1 unit in each case draw x and y axes, taking values of x from -2 to 14 and values of y from 0 to 16. Draw and label triangle X.

(ii) Transformation R is defined as $R: \begin{pmatrix} x \\ y \end{pmatrix} \rightarrow \begin{pmatrix} 2 & 0 \\ 0 & 2 \end{pmatrix} \begin{pmatrix} x \\ y \end{pmatrix}$.

Draw and label the triangle $R(X)$.

(iii) Describe fully the single transformation R.

(iv) Transformation S is defined as $S: \begin{pmatrix} x \\ y \end{pmatrix} \rightarrow \begin{pmatrix} -1.2 & 1.6 \\ 1.6 & 1.2 \end{pmatrix} \begin{pmatrix} x \\ y \end{pmatrix}$.

Draw and label the triangle $S(X)$.

(v) If $S = TR$, describe fully the single transformation T.   [AEB]

8 Draw on graph paper the parallelogram OPQR where O, P, Q and R are respectively the points $(0, 0)$, $(2, 0)$, $(3, 1)$ and $(1, 1)$.

Find and draw the image of OPQR under the transformation whose matrix is $\mathbf{M}$,

where $\mathbf{M} = \begin{pmatrix} 0.8 & -0.6 \\ 0.6 & 0.8 \end{pmatrix}$, and describe this transformation.

Form the product $\mathbf{MN}$, where $\mathbf{N} = \begin{pmatrix} 0.6 & -0.8 \\ 0.8 & 0.6 \end{pmatrix}$ and state what transformation corresponds to $\mathbf{MN}$. Hence or otherwise, find what transformation corresponds to $\mathbf{N}$.   [L]

9 On graph paper, with axes and scales so chosen that x can range at least from 0 to 11 and y at least from -4 to 5, plot the points $O(0, 0)$, $A(1, 0)$, $B(2, 1)$ and $C(0, 1)$ and join them to form a trapezium.

Draw the images of OABC under the transformations represented by the following matrices:

(i) $\mathbf{M} = \begin{pmatrix} 5 & 0 \\ 0 & 5 \end{pmatrix}$: letter this image OA'B'C',

(ii) $\mathbf{N} = \begin{pmatrix} 4 & 3 \\ 3 & -4 \end{pmatrix}$: letter this image OA"B"C".

Describe the transformation connected with $\mathbf{M}$.

OA"B"C" is the image of OA'B'C' under a reflection: draw the invariant line (mirror line) of this reflection, and find its equation.

Describe fully the transformation represented by $\mathbf{N}$.   [L]

10 Two schools A and B have soccer and netball teams. The matrix $\mathbf{X}$ shows the number of players involved in matches whenever the schools play fixtures. The number of matches played in a season is given by the matrix $\mathbf{Y}$. Matrix $\mathbf{Z}$ shows the average transport cost in pence per match for each player.

$$\begin{array}{cc} & \begin{array}{cc} \text{A} & \text{B} \end{array} \\ \begin{array}{c} \text{Soccer} \\ \text{Netball} \end{array} & \begin{pmatrix} 24 & 36 \\ 14 & 21 \end{pmatrix} = \mathbf{X}; \end{array} \quad \begin{array}{c} \text{A} \\ \text{B} \end{array} \begin{pmatrix} 12 \\ 10 \end{pmatrix} = \mathbf{Y}; \quad \begin{array}{c} \text{Cost} \\ \text{(pence)} \end{array} \begin{array}{cc} \text{Soccer} & \text{Netball} \\ (\ 50 & 100 \ ) = \mathbf{Z}. \end{array}$$

(a) Find the matrix products (i) $\mathbf{XY}$,   (ii) $\mathbf{ZX}$,   (iii) $\mathbf{ZXY}$.

(b) Find the total cost of transporting all the players to the matches throughout the season.

(c) In the following season, the total transport costs rose by 20 %. Find the new total transport cost for the following season.   [M]

11 A transformation T is defined by the matrix $\begin{pmatrix} 0 & -1 \\ 1 & 0 \end{pmatrix}$.

(i) Draw axes of x and y on graph paper, taking values of x and y from -5 to $+5$, and mark on the diagram the points $A(0, 3)$ and $B(1, 5)$ and also their images A', B' under the transformation T.

(ii) Describe the geometrical effect of the transformation T.

(iii) Find the gradient of the line segment AB and hence find the equation of the line l through A and B.

(iv) Draw on the diagram the line l', the image of l under T, and find its equation. [JMB]

12 A transformation is defined by $T: \begin{pmatrix} x \\ y \end{pmatrix} \to \begin{pmatrix} 2 \cdot 4 & -1 \cdot 8 \\ 1 \cdot 8 & 2 \cdot 4 \end{pmatrix} \begin{pmatrix} x \\ y \end{pmatrix}$.

(i) Given that $O = (0, 0)$, $A = (4, 0)$, $B = (4, 4)$, $C = (0, 4)$, find the image $O'A'B'C'$ of the square OABC under this transformation and represent the square and its image on a diagram, using a scale of 1 cm : 1 unit on each axis.

(ii) Calculate the length of OA' and the size of angle AOA'.

(iii) Given that T is equivalent to a rotation about O followed by an enlargement, state the angle of the rotation and the scale factor of the enlargement.

(iv) Find the area of O'A'B'C' and the length of A'C'. [JMB]

13 If A, B and C are 2×2 matrices with elements in $\mathbb{R}$, write down which of the following statements are always true and which are not always true:

(a) $\mathbf{AB} = \mathbf{BA}$,

(b) $\mathbf{A(B + C)} = \mathbf{AB} + \mathbf{AC}$,

(c) $\mathbf{A(BC)} = \mathbf{(AB)C}$,

(d) $\mathbf{AB} = \mathbf{O} \Rightarrow \mathbf{A} = \mathbf{O}$ or $\mathbf{B} = \mathbf{O}$, where $\mathbf{O}$ is the 2×2 zero matrix, $\begin{pmatrix} 0 & 0 \\ 0 & 0 \end{pmatrix}$,

(e) the converse of (d).

Give an example to confirm your answer in each case where you think the statement is not always true. [L]

14 (a) Under a certain transformation, the image (x', y') of a point (x, y) is given by

$$\begin{pmatrix} x' \\ y' \end{pmatrix} = \begin{pmatrix} 2 & 1 \\ -1 & 1 \end{pmatrix} \begin{pmatrix} x \\ y \end{pmatrix} + \begin{pmatrix} 3 \\ 9 \end{pmatrix}.$$

(i) Find the coordinates of A, the image of the point $(0, 0)$.

(ii) Find the coordinates of B, the image of the point $(4, 3)$.

(iii) Given that the image of the point (g, h) is the point $(0, 0)$, write down two equations each involving g and h.

Hence or otherwise find the values of g and h.

(b) Find the value of x for which the matrix $\begin{pmatrix} x+3 & 0 \\ 0 & 2 \end{pmatrix}$ (i) has no inverse,

(ii) represents an enlargement.

State the scale factor of this enlargement. [C]

Section 8
Scalar and vector quantities

Some entities require only magnitude (or size) in order to completely describe them; the temperature of a room, the mass of a lump of metal and the time taken to move from one place to another are examples and these entities are called **scalars**.

Some other entities need both magnitude and direction in order to completely describe them; displacement, force, velocity and acceleration are examples and these entities are called **vectors**.

A vector quantity can be represented graphically by a directed line segment and the following notation is used (see Figure 8.1).

Fig. 8.1   Fig. 8.2

In Figure 8.1 the vector represented by the line segment AB, starting at A and finishing at B, is written $\overrightarrow{AB}$. The vector represented by BA, starting at B and finishing at A, is written $\overrightarrow{BA}$ or $-\overrightarrow{AB}$. In writing solutions it is essential to use a notation in which vectors can be easily distinguished from scalars and the reader is advised to use $\overrightarrow{AB}$. When using single small letters the reader is advised to use $\bar{a}$ or $\underset{\sim}{a}$ for the vector printed as **a**. The length of **a** is denoted by $|\mathbf{a}|$.

Addition of vectors

In Figure 8.2, a 'journey from A to B' is equivalent to the sum of 'a journey from A to C' and 'a journey from C to B'. Expressed in vectors this gives $\overrightarrow{AB} = \overrightarrow{AC} + \overrightarrow{CB}$.

Note also $\overrightarrow{AB} = \overrightarrow{AC} - \overrightarrow{BC}$, which explains how vectors are subtracted.

Equality of vectors

Two vectors are equal if, and only if, their magnitudes are equal *and* their directions are the same.

i.e. $\mathbf{a} = \mathbf{b} \Leftrightarrow |\mathbf{a}| = |\mathbf{b}|$ and $\mathbf{a}$ is parallel to $\mathbf{b}$

Deductions:

(a) if $h\mathbf{a} = k\mathbf{b}$ (h, k scalars) then $\mathbf{a}$ is parallel to $\mathbf{b}$; or, if $\mathbf{a}$ and $\mathbf{b}$ are not parallel, $h = 0$ and $k = 0$.

(b) if $l\mathbf{a} + m\mathbf{b} = n\mathbf{a} + p\mathbf{b}$ ($\mathbf{a}$ not parallel to $\mathbf{b}$) then $l = n$ and $m = p$.

In Figure 8.3, the vectors $\mathbf{a}$, $\mathbf{b}$ and $\mathbf{c}$ are equal because they have the same length (magnitude) and the same direction.

Multiplication of a vector by a scalar

The vector $m\mathbf{a}$, where m is a scalar, is parallel to the vector $\mathbf{a}$ and has length (magnitude) m times the vector $\mathbf{a}$. (See Figure 8.4)

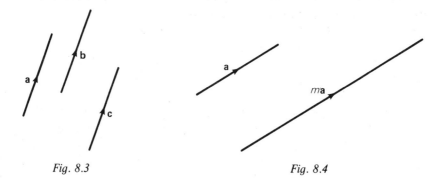

Fig. 8.3   Fig. 8.4

The reader should confirm by using the rules stated previously that the following laws of vector algebra are true:

1 Commutative law $\mathbf{a} + \mathbf{b} = \mathbf{b} + \mathbf{a}$.

2 Associative law $\mathbf{a} + (\mathbf{b} + \mathbf{c}) = (\mathbf{a} + \mathbf{b}) + \mathbf{c} = \mathbf{a} + \mathbf{b} + \mathbf{c}$.

3 Distributive laws $(m + n)\mathbf{a} = m\mathbf{a} + n\mathbf{a}$.

$\qquad\qquad\qquad\qquad m(\mathbf{a} + \mathbf{b}) = m\mathbf{a} + m\mathbf{b}$.

Unit vectors

A unit vector has magnitude *one unit*. In particular, it is customary to take $\mathbf{i}$ and $\mathbf{j}$ as unit vectors parallel to the x-axis and y-axis respectively.

Vectors expressed in terms of components parallel to the coordinate axes

Example 1: Figure 8.5 shows the equal vectors $\overrightarrow{AB}$, $\overrightarrow{CD}$ and $\overrightarrow{OP}$, all of which can be represented by the vector written as $4\mathbf{i} + 3\mathbf{j}$ or as $\begin{pmatrix} 4 \\ 3 \end{pmatrix}$. The

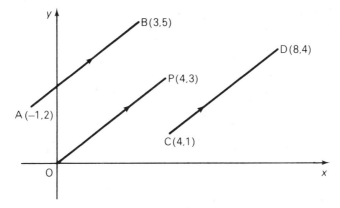

Fig. 8.5

point P, in Figure 8.5, is said to have **position vector** $4\mathbf{i} + 3\mathbf{j}$ and this is used to identify the position, with respect to O as origin and the given coordinate axes, of any point uniquely in the plane of the coordinate axes.

The **magnitude** of $\overrightarrow{OP}$ is $\sqrt{(4^2 + 3^2)} = 5$ units. $[|\overrightarrow{OP}| = 5$ units$]$

The **direction** of $\overrightarrow{OP}$ is defined to be the angle xOP, always measured in a counter-clockwise sense and, in this case $= \arctan \frac{3}{4} = 36 \cdot 9°$.

The following examples illustrate the methods used.

Example 2: *In Figure 8.6, ABCDEF is a regular hexagon, in which* $\overrightarrow{AB} = \mathbf{a}$ *and* $\overrightarrow{AC} = \mathbf{b}$. *Express, in terms of* $\mathbf{a}$ *and* $\mathbf{b}$, (a) $\overrightarrow{BC}$, (b) $\overrightarrow{AD}$, (c) $\overrightarrow{AE}$, (d) $\overrightarrow{AF}$.

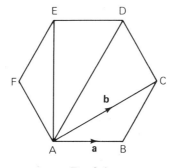

Fig. 8.6

(a) $\overrightarrow{BC} = \overrightarrow{BA} + \overrightarrow{AC} = \overrightarrow{AC} - \overrightarrow{AB} = \mathbf{b} - \mathbf{a}$.
(b) $\overrightarrow{AD} = 2\overrightarrow{BC} = 2(\mathbf{b} - \mathbf{a})$.
(c) $\overrightarrow{AE} = \overrightarrow{AD} + \overrightarrow{DE} = 2(\mathbf{b} - \mathbf{a}) - \mathbf{a} = 2\mathbf{b} - 3\mathbf{a}$.
(d) $\overrightarrow{AF} = \overrightarrow{CD} = \overrightarrow{CA} + \overrightarrow{AD} = -\mathbf{b} + 2(\mathbf{b} - \mathbf{a}) = \mathbf{b} - 2\mathbf{a}$.

Example 3: *Referred to the point O as origin, the position vectors of the*

85

points A, B and C are $(-2\mathbf{i} + 3\mathbf{j})$, $(2\mathbf{i} + 4\mathbf{j})$ *and* $(10\mathbf{i} + 6\mathbf{j})$ *respectively. Prove that the points A, B and C are collinear.*

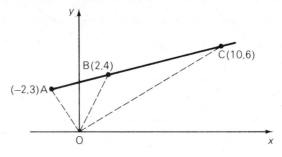

Fig. 8.7

Using Figure 8.7,

$$\overrightarrow{AB} = \overrightarrow{AO} + \overrightarrow{OB} = \overrightarrow{OB} - \overrightarrow{OA} = (2\mathbf{i} + 4\mathbf{j}) - (-2\mathbf{i} + 3\mathbf{j}) = 4\mathbf{i} + \mathbf{j}.$$
$$\overrightarrow{BC} = \overrightarrow{BO} + \overrightarrow{OC} = \overrightarrow{OC} - \overrightarrow{OB} = (10\mathbf{i} + 6\mathbf{j}) - (2\mathbf{i} + 4\mathbf{j}) = 8\mathbf{i} + 2\mathbf{j}.$$

It follows that $\overrightarrow{BC} = 2\overrightarrow{AB}$.

This result implies that $\overrightarrow{BC}$ and $\overrightarrow{AB}$ are in the same direction and, since there is a common point B, the points A, B and C must all lie on the same line; that is the points A, B and C are collinear.

Note also that the magnitude of $\overrightarrow{BC}$ is twice that of $\overrightarrow{AB}$.

Example 4: *The points P and Q are the mid-points of the sides AB and AC respectively of a triangle ABC. Prove that PQ is parallel to BC and that* $PQ = \frac{1}{2}BC$.

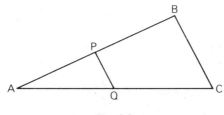

Fig. 8.8

In Figure 8.8, let the position vectors of B and C be $2\mathbf{b}$ and $2\mathbf{c}$ respectively, referred to A as origin.

It follows that $\overrightarrow{AP} = \mathbf{b}$ and $\overrightarrow{AQ} = \mathbf{c}$.

$$\overrightarrow{BC} = \overrightarrow{BA} + \overrightarrow{AC} = \overrightarrow{AC} - \overrightarrow{AB} = 2\mathbf{c} - 2\mathbf{b} = 2(\mathbf{c} - \mathbf{b}).$$
$$\overrightarrow{PQ} = \overrightarrow{PA} + \overrightarrow{AQ} = \overrightarrow{AQ} - \overrightarrow{AP} = \mathbf{c} - \mathbf{b}.$$

Therefore $\overrightarrow{BC} = 2\overrightarrow{PQ}$.

This result implies that $\overrightarrow{BC}$ is parallel to $\overrightarrow{PQ}$ and that $|\overrightarrow{PQ}| = \frac{1}{2}|\overrightarrow{BC}|$.

Note: This result is known in geometry as the **mid-point theorem**.

Exercise 8

1 Given that O has coordinates $(0, 0)$, $\overrightarrow{OA} = \mathbf{a} = \begin{pmatrix} 1 \\ 3 \end{pmatrix}$ and $\overrightarrow{OB} = \mathbf{b} = \begin{pmatrix} 3 \\ 3 \end{pmatrix}$, plot

on graph paper the points A and B and also the points P and Q whose position vectors are $\mathbf{p}$ and $\mathbf{q}$ respectively, where $\mathbf{p} = \frac{1}{2}(\mathbf{a} + \mathbf{b})$ and $\mathbf{q} = \frac{1}{3}(\mathbf{a} + \mathbf{b})$. Describe geometrically the positions of P and Q. [L]

2 $\mathbf{p} = \begin{pmatrix} 1 \\ 0 \end{pmatrix}$, $\mathbf{q} = \begin{pmatrix} 1 \\ 2 \end{pmatrix}$.

(a) Calculate the vector (i) $10\mathbf{q}$, (ii) $\mathbf{p} - \mathbf{q}$.

(b) Find the value of $|\mathbf{q}|$. [CA]

3 The points A and B have position vectors $3\mathbf{i} + 2\mathbf{j}$ and $-\mathbf{i} + 4\mathbf{j}$ respectively, referred to O as origin. The point D has position vector $11\mathbf{i} - 2\mathbf{j}$ and is such that $\overrightarrow{OD} = m\overrightarrow{OA} + n\overrightarrow{OB}$.

Calculate the values of m and n. [L]

4 Given that $\begin{pmatrix} 2 \\ -3 \end{pmatrix} + 3\begin{pmatrix} 5 \\ y \end{pmatrix} = \begin{pmatrix} x \\ y \end{pmatrix}$, find the values of x and y. [C]

5 Given that in the parallelogram ABCD, $\overrightarrow{AB} = \mathbf{a}$, $\overrightarrow{AD} = \mathbf{b}$ and M is the mid-point of DC, express the vector $\overrightarrow{BM}$ in terms of $\mathbf{a}$ and $\mathbf{b}$. [JMB]

6 Given that $\mathbf{a} = \begin{pmatrix} -1 \\ 2 \end{pmatrix}$ and $\mathbf{b} = \begin{pmatrix} 3 \\ 4 \end{pmatrix}$, calculate

(i) $\mathbf{a} + \mathbf{b}$, (ii) $\mathbf{x}$, if $\mathbf{a} + \mathbf{x} = 2\mathbf{b}$, (iii) $|\mathbf{b}|$. [AEB]

7 Given that $\overrightarrow{OA} = \begin{pmatrix} 1 \\ 5 \end{pmatrix}$ and $\overrightarrow{OB} = \begin{pmatrix} 5 \\ -1 \end{pmatrix}$, where O is the origin, show, using the

theorem of Pythagoras, that OA and OB are two sides of a square and find the position vector of the fourth vertex of this square. [L]

8 In the quadrilateral OABC, D is the mid-point of BC and G is the point on AD such that $AG:GD = 2:1$. Given that $\overrightarrow{OA} = \mathbf{a}$, $\overrightarrow{OB} = \mathbf{b}$ and $\overrightarrow{OC} = \mathbf{c}$, express $\overrightarrow{OD}$ and $\overrightarrow{OG}$ in terms of $\mathbf{a}$, $\mathbf{b}$ and $\mathbf{c}$. [L]

9 The vectors $\mathbf{r}$ and $\mathbf{s}$ are not parallel but are such that $|\mathbf{r}| = |\mathbf{s}|$. Find the angle between the vectors $\mathbf{r} + \mathbf{s}$ and $\mathbf{r} - \mathbf{s}$. [C]

10 Given that $\overrightarrow{AB} = \begin{pmatrix} 2 \\ 5 \end{pmatrix}$ and $\overrightarrow{AC} = \begin{pmatrix} 4 \\ 1 \end{pmatrix}$, find $\overrightarrow{BC}$.

Given also that $\overrightarrow{AD} = \begin{pmatrix} 2 \\ 0 \end{pmatrix}$, calculate $\angle DAB$, correct to the nearest degree. [L]

11 The vectors $\mathbf{p}$ and $\mathbf{q}$ are respectively $\begin{pmatrix} 3 \\ 1 \end{pmatrix}$ and $\begin{pmatrix} -1 \\ 3 \end{pmatrix}$. Show that

(i) the magnitudes of $\mathbf{p}$ and $\mathbf{q}$ are the same,

(ii) the directions of $\mathbf{p}$ and $\mathbf{q}$ are at right angles.

Express the vector $\begin{pmatrix} 18 \\ -14 \end{pmatrix}$ in the form $m\mathbf{p} + n\mathbf{q}$, where m and n are real

numbers. [L]

12 The triangles OAB, OCD are such that $\overrightarrow{OA} = \mathbf{a}$, $\overrightarrow{OB} = \mathbf{b}$, $\overrightarrow{OC} = -3\mathbf{a}$, and $\overrightarrow{OD} = -3\mathbf{b}$. Express in terms of $\mathbf{a}$ and $\mathbf{b}$ the vectors $\overrightarrow{AB}$, $\overrightarrow{BC}$, $\overrightarrow{AD}$ and $\overrightarrow{DC}$, and state which of them are in parallel directions.

Describe a transformation which maps triangle OAB onto triangle OCD. [L]

13 ABCD is a quadrilateral with $\overrightarrow{AB} = \mathbf{a}$, $\overrightarrow{BC} = \mathbf{b}$, $\overrightarrow{CD} = \mathbf{c}$, $\overrightarrow{DA} = \mathbf{d}$. Write down an equation connecting $\mathbf{a}$, $\mathbf{b}$, $\mathbf{c}$ and $\mathbf{d}$.

W, X, Y and Z are the mid-points of AB, BC, CD and DA respectively.

Express $\overrightarrow{WX}$ in terms of **a** and **b**, and express $\overrightarrow{ZY}$ in terms of **c** and **d**.

Show that $\overrightarrow{WX} = \overrightarrow{ZY}$, and hence or otherwise that WY and XZ bisect each other. [L]

14 In a velocity triangle drawn to show the flight of an aircraft, the wind-speed is represented in direction and magnitude by the vector **w**, the air-speed and course by the vector **a** and the ground-speed and track by the vector **g**. Write down the vector equation connecting **w**, **a** and **g**.

In the particular case in which **w** and **a** are at right-angles to each other and $|\mathbf{w}| = |\mathbf{a}|$, calculate the ratio $|\mathbf{a}| : |\mathbf{g}|$. [C]

15 In the triangle OAB, X is the mid-point of OA and Y is the mid-point of AB. The lines OY and BX intersect at P. **OA** = **a** and **OB** = **b**.
(a) Express **BX** in terms of **a** and **b**.
(b) Express **BY** in terms of **a** and **b**.
(c) If OP = h OY, express **OP** in terms of h, **a** and **b**.
(d) If BP = k BX, express **BP** in terms of k, **a** and **b**.
(e) By using an appropriate relationship between **OB**, **BP** and **OP** show that
$$\tfrac{1}{2}(h - k)\mathbf{a} = (1 - \tfrac{1}{2}h - k)\mathbf{b}.$$
(f) Deduce two simultaneous equations for h and k and hence find h and k. [CA]

16 P is the middle point of the side BC of the triangle ABC. Q is the middle point of AP, and R is a point on AC such that AR = k. AC, where k is a number. If $\overrightarrow{AB} = \mathbf{a}$, $\overrightarrow{AC} = \mathbf{b}$, give expressions in terms of **a** and **b** for $\overrightarrow{BP}$, $\overrightarrow{AP}$, $\overrightarrow{AQ}$, $\overrightarrow{BQ}$ and $\overrightarrow{BR}$.

Hence find the value of k for which BQR is a straight line, and express your result in the form, 'BQ produced divides AC in the ratio . . .'.

Find also the ratio BQ:QR, when k has the value you have found. [L]

17 OACB is a parallelogram, and OA is produced to D so that AD = OA. If $\overrightarrow{OA} = \mathbf{a}$, $\overrightarrow{OB} = \mathbf{b}$, write down the vectors $\overrightarrow{OC}$ and $\overrightarrow{BD}$ in terms of **a** and **b**.

P is the mid-point of AC. Express in terms of **a** and **b** the vectors $\overrightarrow{BP}$ and $\overrightarrow{PD}$, and state what information your results give concerning the relation of P to the line BD.

X is a point on OC such that OX = $\tfrac{2}{3}$OC. By expressing the vector $\overrightarrow{BX}$ in terms of **a** and **b**, or otherwise, show that X lies on BD and find the ratio in which X divides BD. [L]

18 The vectors **e** and **n** represent velocities of 1 km/h due east and 1 km/h due north respectively. A man rows a boat on a river in such a way that, if there were no current, its velocity would be $2\mathbf{n} - \mathbf{e}$. On a river flowing with velocity $3\mathbf{e}$ the boat's actual velocity is **v**.
(i) Express **v** in the form $a\mathbf{e} + b\mathbf{n}$.
(ii) Calculate $|\mathbf{v}|$. [C]

19 The five points O, P, Q, R and S are so placed that $\overrightarrow{OP} = \mathbf{a}$, $\overrightarrow{PQ} = \tfrac{1}{2}\mathbf{a}$, $\overrightarrow{OR} = \mathbf{b}$ and $\overrightarrow{RS} = \tfrac{1}{3}\mathbf{b}$, where **a** and **b** are vectors in different directions. Express in terms of **a** and **b** the vectors $\overrightarrow{PR}$ and $\overrightarrow{QS}$.

The line QS is produced to X so that SX = 2QS. Show that $\overrightarrow{QX} = 4\mathbf{b} - 4\tfrac{1}{2}\mathbf{a}$, and express $\overrightarrow{OX}$ similarly in terms of **a** and **b**.

Express $\overrightarrow{PX}$ in terms of **a** and **b**, and hence show that X lies on PR produced. Find the ratio in which R divides PX.

Prove that OX is parallel to PS. [L]

20 In the triangle OAB,
M is the point on OA produced such that OM = 3 OA,
N is the point on OB produced such that ON = 2 OB,
P is the point on MN such that MN = 4 MP and
A and T are the points on OM such that $O\hat{A}B = O\hat{T}N = 90°$.

Given that $\mathbf{OA} = \mathbf{a}$ and $\mathbf{OB} = \mathbf{b}$, express in the form $h\mathbf{a} + k\mathbf{b}$
(i) **MN**,   (ii) **MP**,   (iii) **BP**.

Given also that $|\mathbf{a}| = 3$ and $|\mathbf{b}| = 5$, find $|\mathbf{b} - \mathbf{a}|$ and $|\mathbf{MN}|$.   [C]

Section 9
Trigonometry

Right angled triangles

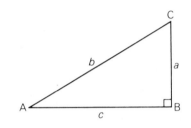

Fig. 9.1

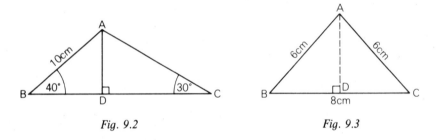

Fig. 9.2   Fig. 9.3

Problems involving right angled triangles are solved by using
either Pythagoras' theorem, which relates the lengths of the three sides,

$$a^2 + c^2 = b^2, \text{ where } b \text{ is the length of the hypotenuse,}$$

or the three basic ratios, sine, cosine and tangent, where

$$\sin (\text{angle}) = \frac{\text{opposite side}}{\text{hypotenuse}}, \qquad \cos (\text{angle}) = \frac{\text{adjacent side}}{\text{hypotenuse}},$$

$$\tan (\text{angle}) = \frac{\text{opposite side}}{\text{adjacent side}}.$$

In the notation of Figure 9.1 the ratios are:

$$\sin A = \frac{a}{b}, \cos A = \frac{c}{b}, \tan A = \frac{a}{c} \text{ and } \sin C = \frac{c}{b}, \cos C = \frac{a}{b}, \tan C = \frac{c}{a}.$$

Note: Sines and cosines are always less than or equal to 1,
$\sin\theta = \cos(90° - \theta)$ for all values of the angle θ,
the converse of Pythagoras' theorem may be used to prove that a
triangle is right-angled when the three sides are given.

Example 1: *In Figure 9.2, $AB = 10\,cm$, $\angle ABD = 40°$, $\angle ACD = 30°$ and
AD is perpendicular to BC. Calculate (a) AD,   (b) DC.*

(a) In $\triangle ABD$, $\sin 40° = \dfrac{AD}{10}$ $\Rightarrow AD = 10\sin 40° = 6\cdot428$ cm.

(b) In $\triangle ADC$, $\tan 60° = \dfrac{DC}{6\cdot428}$ $\Rightarrow DC = 6\cdot428\tan 60° = 11\cdot13$ cm.

An isosceles triangle has one axis of symmetry and this should be made use
of in calculations. In quadrilaterals like the rhombus, kite and arrowhead
(see Section 6) the diagonals intersect at right angles and these properties
should be used in calculations.

Example 2: *In Figure 9.3, $AB = 6\,cm$, $AC = 6\,cm$ and $BC = 8\,cm$; AD is
perpendicular to BC. Calculate the angles of the triangle ABC.*

In $\triangle ABD$, $\sin\angle BAD = \dfrac{4}{6} = 0\cdot6667 \Rightarrow \angle BAD = 41\cdot81°$.

By symmetry $\angle CAD = 41\cdot81°$. Hence $\angle BAC = 83\cdot62°$.
Since the angles of a triangle add up to $180°$,

$$\angle ABC = \angle ACB = 48\cdot19°.$$

Example 3: *In Figure 9.4, C_1 and C_2 are the centres of circles of radii $3\,cm$
and $5\,cm$ respectively, $C_1C_2 = 10\,cm$ and AB is a tangent to both circles, the
contact points being A and B. Calculate the length of AB.*

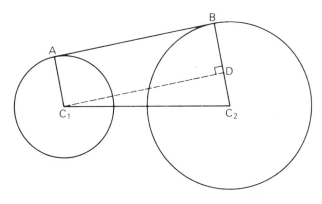

Fig. 9.4

Draw C_1D perpendicular to BC_2 as shown.
   Since C_1A and C_2B are radii and AB is a tangent, the angles at A and B are
each $90°$ and it follows that C_1DBA is a rectangle.

Using Pythagoras' theorem in $\triangle C_1DC_2$, $C_1C_2{}^2 = DC_1{}^2 + DC_2{}^2$.
That is, $AB = C_1D = \sqrt{(10^2 - 2^2)} = \sqrt{96} = 9 \cdot 80$ cm.

Bearings

Bearings are given in degrees, in the range $000°$ to $360°$, measured from north in a clockwise sense.

Example 4: *Three points A, B and C on horizontal ground are such that B bears $030°$ from A and C bears $110°$ from B; $AB = 5$ km and $BC = 4$ km. Calculate the distance and the bearing of C from A.*

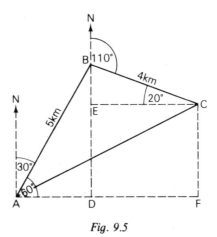

Fig. 9.5

Figure 9.5 illustrates the data and the construction lines which reduce the problem to right-angled triangle calculations.

In $\triangle ABD$, $\cos 60° = \dfrac{AD}{5} \Rightarrow AD \quad = 5 \cos 60° \quad = 2 \cdot 5$ km,

$\qquad\qquad \sin 60° = \dfrac{BD}{5} \Rightarrow BD \quad = 5 \sin 60° \quad = 4 \cdot 330$ km.

In $\triangle BEC$, $\cos 20° = \dfrac{EC}{4} \Rightarrow EC \quad = 4 \cos 20° \quad = 3 \cdot 759$ km,

$\qquad\qquad \sin 20° = \dfrac{BE}{4} \Rightarrow BE \quad = 4 \sin 20° \quad = 1 \cdot 368$ km.

$AF = AD + DF = AD + EC = 6 \cdot 259$ km (the easting of C from A).
$CF = ED \qquad\quad = BD - BE = 2 \cdot 962$ km (the northing of C from A).

Using Pythagoras' theorem, $AC^2 = AF^2 + CF^2 = 47 \cdot 95 \Rightarrow AC = 6 \cdot 924$ km

$$\tan \angle CAF = \frac{CF}{AF} = \frac{2 \cdot 962}{6 \cdot 259} \Rightarrow \angle CAF = 25 \cdot 3°.$$

The bearing of C from A is $064 \cdot 7°$.

Angles of elevation and depression

Example 5: *In Figure 9.6, the points C and D are on the same level and on the same side of the base B of a vertical tower AB, where AB = 100 m. The angle of depression of D from A is 20° and the angle of elevation of A from C is 40°. Calculate the distance DC, given that DCB is a straight line.*

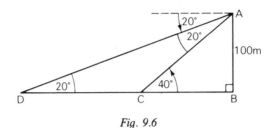

Fig. 9.6

The angle ADC = 20° (alternate angles). The angle DAC = 20° (exterior angle of triangle = sum of interior opposite angles). Hence DC = CA.

In $\triangle$ ABC, $\sin 40° = \dfrac{100}{AC} \Rightarrow AC = \dfrac{100}{\sin 40°} = 155\cdot6$ Hence $DC = 155\cdot6\,m$.

Three-dimensional problems should be broken down into steps involving calculations in plane figures.

Example 6: *The tetrahedron ABCD has edges AB, BC and CA each of length 4 cm and edges DA, DB and DC each of length 6 cm (see Figure 9.7(i)). Calculate, to the nearest degree, (a) the angle made by DB with plane ABC, (b) the angle between planes ACD and ABC.*

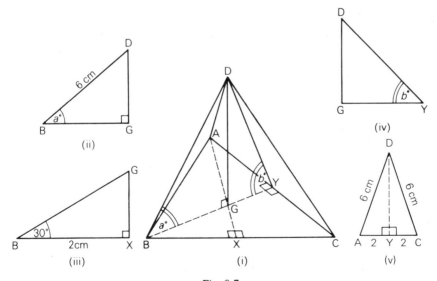

Fig. 9.7

The required angles are marked in Figure 9.7(i) by a and b. The point G, the foot of the perpendicular from D to plane ABC, is equidistant from A, B and C.

In Figure 9.7(iii) $\dfrac{2}{\mathrm{BG}} = \cos 30° \Rightarrow \mathrm{BG} = \dfrac{2}{\cos 30°} = 2\!\cdot\!309\,\mathrm{cm}.$

In Figure 9.7(ii) $\cos a = \dfrac{2\!\cdot\!309}{6} \Rightarrow a = 67\!\cdot\!37°.$

The angle made by DB with plane ABC = 67° (nearest degree).

Figure 9.7(iv) shows angle b; we need to calculate two of the sides of triangle DGY.
In Figure 9.7(v), $\mathrm{DY}^2 = 6^2 - 2^2 = 32 \Rightarrow \mathrm{DY} = 5\!\cdot\!657\,\mathrm{cm}.$
As $\mathrm{GY} = \mathrm{GX}$, from Figure 9.7(iii), $\mathrm{GY} = \mathrm{GX} = 2 \tan 30° = 1\!\cdot\!155\,\mathrm{cm}.$

$$\cos b = \frac{1\!\cdot\!155}{5\!\cdot\!657} \Rightarrow b = 78\!\cdot\!22°.$$

The angle between planes ACD and ABC is 78° (nearest degree).

The general triangle

The solution of the general triangle requires the use of the sine and cosine rules.

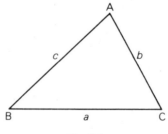

Fig. 9.8

1. Sine Rule

In the notation of Figure 9.8, the sine rule is written as

either $\quad \dfrac{a}{\sin A} = \dfrac{b}{\sin B} = \dfrac{c}{\sin C} \quad$ or $\quad \dfrac{\sin A}{a} = \dfrac{\sin B}{b} = \dfrac{\sin C}{c}.$

2. Cosine Rule

In the notation of Figure 9.8, the cosine rule is written as

either $b^2 = c^2 + a^2 - 2ca \cos B \quad$ or $\quad \cos B = \dfrac{c^2 + a^2 - b^2}{2ca}.$

3. The area of a triangle

Area of $\triangle \mathrm{ABC} = \tfrac{1}{2}ca \sin B.$

Trigonometric ratios of obtuse angles

$\sin \theta = \sin (180° - \theta)$ and for example $\sin 132° = \sin 48°$.

$\cos \theta = -\cos (180° - \theta)$ and for example $\cos 132° = -\cos 48°$.

$\tan \theta = -\tan (180° - \theta)$ and for example $\tan 132° = -\tan 48°$.

The graphs of $y = \sin x$, $y = \cos x$ and $y = \tan x$ can be used to prove these formulae and to find the values of ratios whose angles lie outside the interval $0 \leqslant \theta \leqslant 180°$.

In the following examples which illustrate the use of the formulae given above, the reader is advised to draw a separate diagram each time and write in the given data, which refer to a triangle ABC.

Example 1: *Given that $B = 60°$, $C = 40°$ and $a = 4\,cm$, find b.*

The angle $A = 180° - 60° - 40° = 80°$ (third angle of triangle).

Using the sine rule we have

$$\frac{b}{\sin 60°} = \frac{4}{\sin 80°}$$

$$\Rightarrow b = \frac{4 \sin 60°}{\sin 80°} = 3·518.$$

The length of AC is $3·518\,cm$.

Example 2: *Given that $b = 6\,cm$, $c = 8\,cm$ and $B = 45°$, find C.*

Using the sine rule we have, $\dfrac{\sin C}{8} = \dfrac{\sin 45°}{6}$

$$\Rightarrow \sin C = \frac{8 \sin 45°}{6} = 0·9428 \quad \text{and} \quad C = 70·53° \; or \; 109·47°.$$

The reader is advised to draw the triangle accurately and confirm that two possible solutions arise.

Note: If C had been given as 45° instead of B for $b = 6\,cm$ and $c = 8\,cm$, the resulting angle B would only have one value, which must be less than 45° because $b < c$, thus making B < C.

This value is given by $\sin B = \dfrac{6 \sin 45°}{8} = 0·5303 \Rightarrow B = 32·03°.$

Example 3: *Given that $a = 3\,cm$, $c = 4\,cm$ and $B = 60°$, find b.*

Using the cosine rule we have, $b^2 = 4^2 + 3^2 - 2 \times 4 \times 3 \cos 60°$

$$b^2 = 16 + 9 - 12 = 13$$
$$b = 3·606.$$

The length of BC is $3·606\,cm$

Note: It is useful to consider the cosine rule used in this way as an extension of the theorem of Pythagoras. If the given angle is less than $90°$, there is a quantity to subtract on the right hand side; if the angle is greater than $90°$, the $-$ sign will change to $+$ as the cosine of an obtuse angle is negative.

Example 4: *Given that $a = 7$, $b = 5$ and $c = 4$, the units being in metres, find A.*

Using the cosine rule we have,

$$\cos A = \frac{5^2 + 4^2 - 7^2}{2 \times 5 \times 4} = \frac{25 + 16 - 49}{40} = -\frac{1}{5} = -0\cdot 2.$$

The $-$ sign indicates that A is obtuse.

$$A = 180° - 78\cdot 46° = 101\cdot 54°.$$

Example 5: *Given that $a = 5$ cm, $c = 4$ cm and $B = 50°$, find the area of $\triangle ABC$.*

$$\text{Area of } \triangle ABC = \tfrac{1}{2} \times 4 \times 5 \times \sin 50° = 7\cdot 66 \, cm^2.$$

Summary

When two angles and the length of a side are given, use the sine rule to find the other sides.
When two sides and a non-included angle are given, use the sine rule to find a second angle, *but remember there may be two solutions.*
When two sides and the included angle are given, use the cosine rule to find the third side.
When three sides are given, use the cosine rule to find an angle.

Two important identities

1. $\tan \theta \equiv \dfrac{\sin \theta}{\cos \theta}.$

2. $\sin^2 \theta + \cos^2 \theta \equiv 1.$

These identities are true for ALL values of θ.

Example 6: *Given that the angle A is obtuse and $\cos A = \dfrac{-5}{13}$, find the values of (a) $\sin A$, (b) $\tan A$.*

(a) Using 2 above, $\sin^2 A = 1 - \left(\dfrac{-5}{13}\right)^2 = 1 - \dfrac{25}{169} = \dfrac{144}{169}.$

If A is obtuse, $\sin A > 0$, and this gives $\sin A = \dfrac{12}{13}.$

(b) Using 1 above, $\tan A = \dfrac{\sin A}{\cos A} = \left(\dfrac{12}{13}\right) \div \left(\dfrac{-5}{13}\right)$

$$= \dfrac{-12}{5}.$$

Exercise 9.1

In your answers give angles to 1 decimal place and lengths to 3 significant figures.

1   The following sets of data refer to a triangle ABC, where B = 90°. Draw a labelled diagram in each case and calculate the side or angle given in the brackets:
   (a) BC = 5 cm, angle BAC = 60°;   (b) AC = 8 cm, angle ACB = 48°;
   (AB),   (BC),
   (c) AB = 4·9 cm, angle   (d) AC = 10·8 cm, BC = 4·2 cm;
   ACB = 20°; (AC),   (AB),
   (e) AC = 6·5 cm, BC = 1·3 cm;   (f) BC = 3 cm, AB = 2 cm;
   (angle BAC),   (angle ACB).

2   The angles of a right-angled triangle are in the ratios $1:2:3$ and the length of the hypotenuse is 10 cm. Calculate the lengths of the other sides.

3   Given that one unit on each coordinate axis is 1 cm, calculate the distance between the points with coordinates (1, 2) and (4, 6).

4   In triangle ABC, C = 90° and $\tan A = \dfrac{x}{y}$. Find, in terms of x and y, (a) tan B, (b) sin A, (c) cos B.

5   In triangle ABC, C = 90°, B = 60° and AC = 20 cm. The bisector of angle B meets AC at D. Calculate the length of DC.

6   A ladder, of length 10 m, has one end resting against a vertical wall and the other end resting on horizontal ground at a distance 2 m from the wall. The vertical plane containing the ladder is at right angles to the wall. Calculate the angle made by the ladder with the vertical. The ladder is moved so that it rests in the same vertical plane with the top 1 m lower than in the first position. Calculate how far the foot of the ladder has moved from its first position.

7   A rhombus ABCD has diagonals of lengths 12 cm and 16 cm. Calculate the length of a side of this rhombus and its angles.

8   The medians AD, BE, CF of an equilateral triangle ABC meet at G. Given that AB = 6 cm, calculate the length of GD.

9   In the kite ABCD, AB = AD = 6 cm, CB = CD = 9 cm and BD = 8 cm. Calculate the angles of the kite and the length of AC.

10   AB and CD are parallel chords of lengths 6 cm and 7 cm respectively in a circle of radius 10·4 cm. If E and F are the mid-points of the chords, calculate the possible lengths of EF.

11   Calculate the length of a chord which subtends an angle of 47° at the circumference of a circle of radius 6·5 cm.

12   In the quadrilateral ABCD, angles ABC and DCB are each 90°, AB = 5 cm and AD = DC = 8 cm. Calculate the area of the quadrilateral ABCD.

13   To reach a point B from a point A a hiker should travel 4 km on a bearing 050°. If he were to travel on a bearing of 060° for 2 km from A before realising his error, calculate how far he would then be west of B.

14   The foot B of a vertical tower BD, of height 25 m, is at the same level as the points A and C, where A is 50 m south of B and C is due east of B. The angle of elevation of D from C is 50°. Calculate the distance between A and C.

15   In Figure 9.9 (overleaf), $\angle BAC = 30°$, $\angle ABD = \angle AXD = 90°$, AB = 10 cm and BD = 5 cm. Calculate the length of DX.

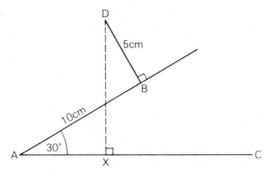

Fig. 9.9

16 Figure 9.10 shows a cuboid with AB = 5 cm, BC = 3 cm and GC = 2 cm; X is the mid-point of DC; J is the mid-point of HG. Calculate the length of the diagonal AG.

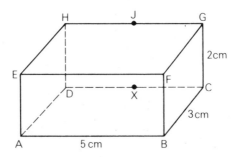

Fig. 9.10

For each of the following, state the angle required and then calculate it:
(a) the angle between AG and the face ABCD,
(b) the angle between AG and the face ADHE,
(c) the angle between AJ and the face DCGH,
(d) the angle between the planes ADGF and ABCD.

17 For each of the following sets of data for a triangle ABC calculate the value of x:
(a) AB = 4 cm, BC = 6 cm, ∠ABC = 30°, AC = x cm,
(b) AB = 3 cm, AC = 5 cm, ∠ABC = 60°, ∠ACB = x°,
(c) AB = 4 cm, AC = 5 cm, BC = 2 cm, ∠ACB = x°,
(d) AB = 9 cm, AC = 8 cm, ∠ACB = 75°, ∠BAC = x°,
(e) BC = 12 cm, ∠BAC = 70°, ∠ABC = 50°, AB = x cm,
(f) AB = 2 cm, AC = 1 cm, ∠ABC = 27°, ∠ACB = x°,
(g) AB = 5·2 cm, AC = 4·6 cm, ∠ABC = 40°, ∠ACB = x°,
(h) AB = 8 cm, BC = 2·5 cm, ∠ABC = 110°, AC = x cm,
(i) AC = 7 cm, ∠BAC = 95°, ∠ABC = 20°, BC = x cm,
(j) AB = 3 cm, AC = 4 cm, BC = 6 cm, ∠BAC = x°.

18 In the quadrilateral ABCD, AB = 4 cm, BC = 5 cm, AD = 6 cm, DC = 7 cm and ∠ADC = 80°. Calculate (a) AC, (b) ∠ABC, (c) the area of ABCD.

19 In the △ABC, AB = 4 cm, BC = 6 cm and AC = 5 cm. Calculate (a) the smallest angle in △ABC, (b) the area of △ABC.

20 A triangle with area 12 cm² has two sides of lengths 4 cm and 12 cm. Calculate the possible values of the angle between the given sides.

Exercise 9.2

1 In the rectangle ABCD, the side AB = 12 cm and the diagonal AC = 16 cm. Calculate (i) the side AD, (ii) the acute angle between the diagonals. [O]

2 In $\triangle$ABC, the angle at C is a right angle, $\hat{\text{BAC}}$ = 66° and AC = 20·0 cm. Calculate
(i) BC, (ii) the area of the triangle. [C]

3 A man observes the angle of elevation of the top of a tower to be 26°. The height of the tower is known to be 45 m. Neglecting the height of the man, how far is he from the foot of the tower? [L]

4 A man leaves X and walks 2·3 km due west to Y. From Y he walks 7·5 km due south to Z. Calculate the bearing of Z from X. [AEB]

5 In the triangle PQS, the line QR is perpendicular to PS, and T is the mid-point of QR. Given that $\hat{\text{PQR}}$ = 40°, ST = 4 cm and RT = TQ = 2 cm, calculate
(i) PR, (ii) PQ, (iii) cos $\hat{\text{RTS}}$, (iv) SQ. [C]

6 An equilateral triangle is inscribed in a circle of radius 5 cm. Calculate the length of a side of the triangle, giving your answer in centimetres correct to one place of decimals. [JMB]

7 A thin rectangular sheet of metal ABCD has AB = 25 cm. A point P on DC is such that AP = 18 cm and the angle PAB = 72° 30′. Calculate
(i) the length PB, (ii) the area of the triangle PAB. Hence write down the area of the rectangle ABCD and calculate the length AD.

Another point Q is taken on the edge DC such that DQ = DA. Calculate the area of the triangle QAD. [AEB]

8 A surveyor observes that, in a level field OPQR, P is due east of O, Q is on a bearing 340° from P, OP = 60 m and PQ = 96 m. He notes also that $\triangle$ OQR is equilateral. Calculate (a) the length OQ, (b) the bearing of R from O, (c) the area, in hectares, of the field, given that 1 hectare = 10^4 m². [L]

9 XYZ is a triangle right-angled at X. The side YZ = 10 cm and neither of the other sides is less than 4 cm long. Calculate (a) the greatest and least possible values of the angle Y, (b) the greatest possible area of the triangle. [L]

10 In the acute-angled triangle ABC, AB = 8 cm, AC = 6 cm and the area of the triangle is 21 cm². Calculate angle A. [L]

11 In a triangle ABC, BC = 16 cm and $\angle$ABC = 55°. The foot of the perpendicular from A to BC is D and AD = 10 cm. Calculate (i) BD, (ii) CD, (iii) $\angle$ACB. [O]

12 PQ is a diameter of a circle of radius 5 cm and PS is a chord of length 8 cm. R is a point on PQ produced so that QR = 7 cm. Calculate (a) sin PQS, (b) the length of QS, (c) the area of $\triangle$QRS. [L]

13 In $\triangle$ABC, BC = 5 cm, $\angle$BAC = 30° and $\angle$BCA = 72°. Calculate the length of AB. [L]

14 The diagonals PR and QS of the quadrilateral PQRS intersect at right angles at the point O. If OP = 10 cm, OQ = 8 cm, RS = 18 cm and $\angle$OQR = 54° calculate, (a) OR, (b) QR, (c) $\angle$QPR, (d) $\angle$PRS. [L]

15 Given that $x°$ is an acute angle and tan $x°$ = $\frac{12}{5}$, find, without using tables, leaving your answers as fractions,
(a) sin $x°$, (b) cos (180° − $x°$). [L]

16 Given that α is an obtuse angle and sin α = $\frac{8}{17}$, find, without using tables or a calculator, the values of cos α and tan α. [L]

17 X and Y are supplementary angles. If X is the acute angle whose sine is $\frac{5}{13}$, find, without using tables, the value of (a) cos X, (b) cos Y. [L]

18 (a) Given that cos $x°$ = $-$ cos 72°, state two possible values of x.
(b) In triangle ABC, cos A = $-\frac{1}{9}$, AB = c = 7 cm and AC = b = 9 cm. Calculate (i) the numerical value of $2bc$ cos A, (ii) the length of BC. [C]

19 A parallelogram has sides of length 9 cm and 5 cm and one of its angles is 112°. Calculate the length of the longer diagonal. [AEB]

20 A man walking due north along a beach sights from a point P the northern tip X of an island at a bearing of 315°. One mile further along the beach the bearing of X from his new position Q is 290°. Calculate the distance XQ.

One mile further along the beach, the man is at R. Calculate the distance XR. Calculate the shortest distance of X from the path of the man.   [O]

21 In making a map, a surveyor notes that the three points P, Q and R are at the same level, Q is due east of P, and R is to the north of the line PQ.

He finds that PQ = 6 km, QR = 8 km and RP = 7 km. Calculate $R\hat{P}Q$ and the bearing of R from P.

The point S lies inside △ PQR and is such that the bearing of S from P is 020° and that of S from Q is 300°. Calculate $S\hat{P}Q$, $S\hat{Q}P$ and the distance PS.   [C]

22 The horizontal base of a pyramid V ABC is an equilateral triangle ABC, of side 12 cm, and the vertex V is vertically above the point C. The slant edges V A and V B are each of length 14 cm, and X is the foot of the perpendicular from V to AB.

Calculate (i) VC, (ii) VX, (iii) the angle made by VA with the horizontal, (iv) the angle made by the face V AB with the horizontal.   [C]

23 A pyramid rests with its square base ABCD on a horizontal plane. Its vertex V is vertically above the centre of its base. If AB = 12 cm and VA = 16 cm, calculate (a) ∠AVB, (b) AC, (c) the angle between the base ABCD and the sloping face V AB.   [L]

24 C is the foot of a vertical tower 30 m high. A is a point due south of the tower from which the angle of elevation of the top of the tower is 17°. B is a point due west of the tower from which the angle of elevation of the top of the tower is 32°. Given that A, B, and C are all in the same horizontal plane, calculate (i) the length of AC, (ii) the length of BC, (iii) the bearing of B from A.

P is the point on AB which is nearest to C. Calculate the angle of elevation of the top of the tower from P.   [JMB]

25 From a point R at the top of a vertical cliff 200 m above sea level two ships P and Q can be seen out at sea. Ship P is due east of R and Ship Q is due north of R. The angles of depression of P and Q from R are 10° and 25° respectively. Calculate (i) the distances, correct to the nearest 10 metres, of P and Q from the point at sea level vertically below R, (ii) the distance, correct to the nearest 10 metres, of Q from P, (iii) the bearing, to the nearest degree, of Q from P.   [JMB]

Section 10
Statistics and probability

Statistics is concerned with collection, presentation and interpretation of data. The data can be either **quantitative** or **qualitative** and numerical data can be either **continuous** or **discrete**.

Example: Consider an international men's 100 metre invitation race. The nationality of each competitor is a qualitative variable. The number of runners taking part in each heat of the race is a whole number (discrete) variable. The time taken by each competitor to complete a heat of the race could take any value between say 10 s and 13 s and is a continuous variable. The values taken by a continuous variable are often placed in class intervals to form what is called a frequency distribution.

Graphical presentation of data

Example 1: *Out of £90 a family spends £15 on their house, £40 on food, £10 on travelling and the remainder on entertainment.*
 Display this information (a) on a bar chart, (b) on a pie chart.

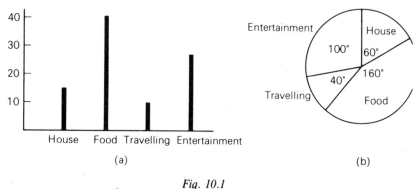

Fig. 10.1

In Figure 10.1(a), the height of each bar represents the frequency and the width of each bar is irrelevant being merely a matter of choice.
 In Figure 10.1(b), the angle at the centre for each sector is calculated.

Spending on the house: angle $= \dfrac{15}{90} \times 360° = 60°$, and similarly for the other sectors.

Example 2: *The masses, measured to the nearest kg, of 100 sheep are shown in the table.*

Mass (kg)	65–74	75–79	80–84	85–89	90–99
No. of sheep	20	20	40	10	10

Draw a histogram to display these data.

Since mass is a continuous variable and each value has been rounded to the nearest whole number, the lengths of the class intervals are
$$10, \quad 5, \quad 5, \quad 5, \quad 10,$$
respectively. (*Note*: the first interval runs from 64·5 to 74·5 giving length 10.)

For a histogram the height of each rectangle must ensure *that its area is proportional to the frequency* for that class interval. Hence the respective heights are 2, 4, 8, 2, 1. Figure 10.2 shows the histogram.

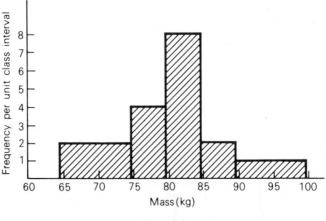

Fig. 10.2

Measures of central position

Three important measures of central position for a list of numbers or a frequency distribution are the **mean**, the **median** and the **mode**.

(a) The mean

The mean is the common average obtained by dividing the total sum of all the members in the list or distribution by the frequency.

102

(b) The median

The median is obtained by writing the list in order of size and selecting the middle number when the total frequency is odd, or the two middle numbers when the total frequency is even. In the first case, the median is the middle member and in the second case the median is the mean of the two middle members.

(c) The mode

For a list of numbers, the mode is the number which occurs most often.

Example 3: *Find (a) the mean, (b) the median, (c) the mode of the numbers*
6, 5, 3, 14, 9, 15, 3, 5, 12, 7, 12, 5.

(a) Mean = sum of the numbers $\div 12 = \dfrac{96}{12} = 8$.

(b) Rearrange in order 3, 3, 5, 5, 5, 6, 7, 9, 12, 12, 14, 15.
Middle members are 6 and 7. Hence median = $\frac{1}{2}(6 + 7) = 6 \cdot 5$.

(c) The number 5 occurs most often. Hence mode = 5.

Example 4: *Estimate, in kg, (a) the mean mass, (b) the median mass of the frequency distribution given in Example 2.*

(a) The mid-point of each class interval is chosen to represent the members in that interval when estimating the mean of the distribution.

Mid-interval value (kg)	69·5	77	82	87	94·5
Frequency	20	20	40	10	10

Estimate of mean = $\dfrac{69 \cdot 5 \times 20 + 77 \times 20 + 82 \times 40 + 87 \times 10 + 94 \cdot 5 \times 10}{100}$

$= 80 \cdot 25$.

(b) If the 100 sheep could be lined up in mass order, the median mass would be obtained by finding the mean of the masses of the sheep in the 50th and 51st positions. As this is impossible, an estimate of the median only can be obtained. This can be achieved by two possible approaches; the median bisects the total area under the complete histogram of the distribution, or the estimate can be obtained by drawing a cumulative frequency distribution curve.

First approach: The median lies in the interval 79·5 to 84·5 and let us suppose it divides this interval into two parts x and $5 - x$.

Since the areas on the two sides of the histogram are equal,

$$20 + 20 + 8x = (5 - x)8 + 10 + 10 \text{ giving } x = 1 \cdot 25.$$

Estimate of median = $79 \cdot 5 + 1 \cdot 25$ kg = $80 \cdot 75$ kg.

Second approach: The cumulative frequency distribution is formed.

Mass		64·5	74·5	79·5	84·5	89·5	99·5
Cumulative freq.		0	20	40	80	90	100

The cumulative frequency graph, called the ogive, is given (see Figure 10.3).

Note: An indication only is given for the solution using the second approach. The reader is expected to draw an accurate graph to obtain the estimate for the median which is given.

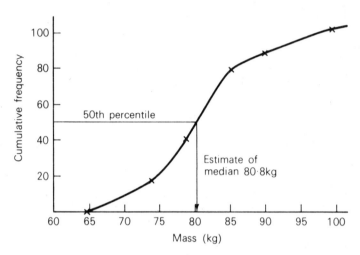

Fig. 10.3 (not to scale)

Examples and notes on probability

Example 1:   *A card is to be selected at random from a normal pack of 52 playing cards. Find the probability that the card selected will be (a) red, (b) an ace, (c) a red ace.*

There are 52 cards, each of which has probability $\dfrac{1}{52}$ of being selected.

(a) There are 26 red cards,   P (red) $= \dfrac{26}{52} = \dfrac{1}{2}.$

(b) There are 4 aces,   P (ace) $= \dfrac{4}{52} = \dfrac{1}{13}.$

(c) There are 2 red aces,   P (red ace) $= \dfrac{2}{52} = \dfrac{1}{26}.$

Note: Let A be the event 'a red card is selected' and let B be the event 'an ace is selected'. The event 'a red ace is selected' implies that the events A and B will occur simultaneously and is denoted by AB.

In this case, we see that $P(AB) = P(A) \times P(B)$ and, when this happens, the events A and B are said to be **independent**.

Conversely, given that A and B are independent events, it follows that

$$P(AB) = P(A) \times P(B).$$

Example 2: *Two beads are to be drawn, one at a time, at random and with replacement from a bag containing 5 red, 3 yellow and 7 blue beads. Find the probability that, for the two beads so selected, (a) the first will be red and the second will be blue, (b) both will be yellow.*

Since the first bead is to be replaced before the second bead is drawn, the two drawings are independent and from the same sample space.

(a) P (first will be red and second will be blue $= \dfrac{5}{15} \times \dfrac{7}{15} = \dfrac{7}{45}$.

(b) P (both will be yellow) $= \dfrac{3}{15} \times \dfrac{3}{15} = \dfrac{1}{25}$.

Example 3: *Repeat Example 2 given that the first bead is NOT replaced before the second is drawn.*

The previous solution needs adjustment because the second drawing is conditional on what happened in the first.

(a) P (first will be red and second will be blue) $= \dfrac{5}{15} \times \dfrac{7}{14} = \dfrac{1}{6}$.

(b) P (both will be yellow) $= \dfrac{3}{15} \times \dfrac{2}{14} = \dfrac{1}{35}$.

Example 4: *An unbiased penny is to be tossed twice. Find the probability that at least one head will show.*

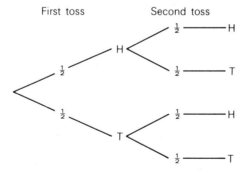

Fig. 10.4   Tree diagram

The sample space consists of 4 simple events, these being

Sample space	HH	HT	TH	TT
Probability	$\frac{1}{4}$	$\frac{1}{4}$	$\frac{1}{4}$	$\frac{1}{4}$

Each of these 4 events is **mutually exclusive**, that is, if one occurs, the others cannot occur.

P (at least one head) $= P(HH) + P(HT) + P(TH) = \frac{1}{4} + \frac{1}{4} + \frac{1}{4} = \frac{3}{4}$.

Note: The events 'no heads occur' and 'at least one head occurs' are also *mutually exclusive* and their union is the complete sample space.
Using this approach, the solution to Example 4 reduces to
P (at least one head) $= 1 - P(TT) = 1 - \frac{1}{4} = \frac{3}{4}$.

Example 5: *The independent probabilities that Anne and Betty will serve an ace in tennis are $\frac{1}{10}$ and $\frac{1}{12}$ respectively. Each girl is to serve once. Find the probability that one and only one girl will serve an ace.*

Let A be the event 'Anne serves an ace' and let B be the event 'Betty serves an ace'.

From data $P(A) = \frac{1}{10}$, $P(A') = \frac{9}{10}$, $P(B) = \frac{1}{12}$ and $P(B') = \frac{11}{12}$.

(**Note:** The event A' is the complement of event A, that is $P(A) + P(A') = 1$.)
P (one and only one girl will serve an ace) $= P(AB') + P(A'B)$
$$= P(A)P(B') + P(A')P(B)$$
$$= \frac{1}{10} \times \frac{11}{12} + \frac{9}{10} \times \frac{1}{12}$$
$$= \frac{20}{120}$$
$$= \frac{1}{6}.$$

Note: When two events A and B are mutually exclusive

$$P(A + B) = P(A) + P(B).$$

When two events A and B are independent

$$P(AB) = P(A)P(B).$$

Exercise 10

1 The sales of two commodities, x kg of A and y kg of B, are represented by a pie-chart.
(i) If the angle of the sector representing the sale of A is 60°, write down the value of $\frac{x}{y}$.
(ii) If, however, $x = 80$ and the angle of the sector representing the sale of A is 160°, find y.   [C]

2 The numbers of weed seeds in 100 similar packets of flower seeds are shown below.

No. of weed seeds	0	1	2	3	4	5	6	7	8
No. of packets	5	17	25	19	13	12	5	2	2

Determine (a) the median, (b) the mode, (c) the range.   [AEB]

3 The masses of thirty ten-week-old gerbils are summarised below.

Mass (g)	38–	40–	42–	44–	48–
Number of gerbils	13	9	5	3	0

(i) Write down the mid-value of each of the first four classes.
(ii) Estimate the arithmetic mean of the masses, giving your answer to three significant figures.   [AEB]

4 A set of five numbers has mode 4 and mean $6\frac{1}{2}$. Given that three members of the set are 3, 4 and 7, find the other two members of the set. State the median value of the five members.   [L]

5 On a certain farm there are 36 cows, 24 pigs, 75 sheep and 45 chickens. Sketch a pie chart to represent this information, marking the size of the angle in each sector.   [JMB]

6 The distribution of the number of examination passes gained by a group of 100 students is shown in the following table.

Number of examination passes	1	2	3	4	5	6
Number of students	12	15	24	26	15	8

For this distribution, find (i) the mode, (ii) the median. (iii) the mean.   [C]

7

Method of travel	Bus	Train	Walking	Car	Bicycle
Number of boys	9	3	6	2	7

Draw a pie chart to illustrate the figures, shown above, obtained by a boy doing such a survey from a class of 27 boys. State the relative frequency of those who travel to school by train.

If a boy is chosen at random from the class, find the probability that he travels to school by bus.   [L]

8 The number of eggs in 100 birds' nests are as follows:

Number of eggs	2	3	4	5	6	7
Frequency	5	30	25	25	10	5

(i) State the modal number of eggs for the distribution.
(ii) Find the median.
(iii) Calculate the mean number of eggs per nest.
(iv) For a further 20 nests the mean was 3·0 eggs per nest. Calculate the mean number of eggs for all 120 nests.   [AEB]

9 The arithmetic mean of five scores in a game is 12·2. When a sixth score is included, the mean decreases to 12. Find the sixth score.   [JMB]

10

Mark	0	1	2	3	4	5	6	7	8	9	10
Frequency	2	3	3	5	5	6	11	8	3	3	1

The marks scored by 50 candidates in a spelling test are given on page 107. Calculate (a) the arithmetic mean, (b) the median, (c) the interquartile range, for this set of marks.

Given that ten more candidates take the test and the new arithmetic mean, for the total of 60 candidates, is 5·3, find the arithmetic mean of the marks of these ten candidates. [L]

11 In illustrating grouped frequency tables, what is the difference between a bar chart and a histogram? Using graph paper, draw accurate histograms to illustrate the following two sets of data taking care to label the axes correctly.

(a) Marks out of 50 for a test taken by 30 children:

Range	0–9	10–19	20–29	30–39	40–49
Frequency	2	6	10	8	4

(b) Heights of 50 plants in centimetres correct to the nearest centimetre:

Range	0–19	20–29	30–34	35–38	40–49
Frequency	4	6	14	16	10

State what geometric property the median has in relation to the histogram and use this fact to mark in accurately the median on your diagram illustrating Table (b). [L].

12 The cumulative distribution of marks gained by a group of 60 pupils in an examination is given in the table below.

Mark	10	20	30	35	40	45	50	65
Number of candidates who gained less than this mark	0	4	12	23	38	48	53	60

Using a vertical scale of 2 cm to represent 10 candidates and a horizontal scale of 2 cm to represent 10 marks, plot these values and draw a smooth curve through your points.

(i) Use your graph to estimate the median mark and the inter-quartile range.

Grade E was awarded to pupils scoring less than 30 marks and Grade A to those scoring 50 marks or more.

(ii) A pupil was selected at random from the sixty. Find the probability that (a) the pupil was awarded Grade E, (b) the pupil was awarded either Grade E or Grade A.

(iii) Two pupils were selected at random from the sixty. Find the probability that they were both awarded Grade E.

Give your answers to (ii) and (iii) as fractions in their lowest terms. [C]

13 A group of 50 boys each threw a dart at a dartboard and each measured the distance in centimetres (to the nearest millimetre) of the tip of his dart from the centre of the board. They recorded the following results.

0·5	6·5	8·4	3·6	2·8	6·6	7·3	9·2	8·1	4·9
5·1	4·1	8·0	6·1	9·2	4·4	5·9	7·9	5·8	6·2
12·1	8·3	4·9	1·1	8·4	10·2	8·1	5·7	11·2	4·7
6·1	5·1	9·0	4·8	4·2	5·1	9·1	5·1	8·9	7·8
7·2	8·3	4·3	6·3	7·5	6·4	7·8	6·1	7·1	6·5

(i) Make a grouped frequency distribution of these results using classes of 0·0–, 2·0–, 4·0–, 6·0–, 8·0–, 10·0–, 12·0–13·9.

(ii) Draw a cumulative frequency polygon to illustrate the grouped frequency distribution.

(iii) By using your diagram, or otherwise, estimate the median and the quartiles.

(iv) Estimate the percentage of boys whose throws were less than 6·5 cm from the centre. [JMB]

14 A coin is biased in such a way that, when it is tossed, heads is twice as likely to occur as tails. Find the probability that (i) when the coin is tossed once, heads occur, (ii) when the coin is tossed twice, either two heads or two tails occur. [AEB]

15 (a) A bag contained 6 balls numbered from one to six. One ball was drawn at random from the bag, the number on it was noted and it was then replaced. In an experiment the scores for 50 draws were recorded as follows:

Score	1	2	3	4	5	6
Number of times it occurred	6	10	11	15	7	1

(i) Write down the modal score.

(ii) Find the median score.

(iii) Calculate the mean score.

(iv) For this experiment, calculate the probability that a particular score was greater than three.

(b) A fair cubical die with faces numbered 1 to 6 is thrown and a fair coin is tossed. Calculate (i) the probability of obtaining a two *and* a head, (ii) the probability of obtaining *neither* a two *nor* a head. [CA]

16 Delegates for a conference are to be selected at random from a committee of 7 men and 3 women. Find the probability that

(a) the first delegate selected will be a woman,

(b) the first two delegates selected will be women,

(c) at least one of the first two delegates will be a woman,

(d) a particular married couple (both members of the committee) will be selected as the first two delegates. [L]

17 (a) Given that $A = \{2, 4, 6\}$, $B = \{3, 5, 7\}$ and $C = \left\{\dfrac{a}{b} : a \in A, b \in B\right\}$, list the nine elements of the set C.

List the elements which are (i) less than $\frac{1}{2}$, (ii) greater than 1.

Hence state as a fraction the probability that an element of C chosen at random is *either* less than $\frac{1}{2}$ *or* greater than 1.

(b) Four cards are marked $\boxed{1}$, $\boxed{2}$, $\boxed{3}$, $\boxed{4}$.

(i) Two cards are chosen at the same time from these four. State the number of possible choices.

Find the probability that when two cards are chosen at random from these four, the card marked 4 is one of them.

(ii) One card is chosen, its marking is noted and then it is replaced. Once again a card is chosen and its marking noted. Find the probability that (a) the same card is chosen twice, (b) the sum of the numbers on the two chosen cards is 6. [C]

18 The independent events A and B occur with probability $\frac{1}{4}$ and $\frac{2}{3}$ respectively. Calculate the probability that (a) A and B both occur, (b) A or B or both occur, (c) A occurs and B does not occur. [L]

19 (a) Find how many different numbers can be obtained by addition of any two numbers chosen from the set $\{1, 2, 3, 4, 5, 6\}$.
(b) The six digits in the set $\{1, 2, 3, 4, 5, 6\}$ are placed in a bag, and two of them are picked out unseen. Find the probability that when added together the result is (i) 7, (ii) 10. [M]

20 (i) $\mathscr{E} = \{(x, y): x$ and y are positive integers$\}$,
$A = \{(x, y): 1 \leqslant x \leqslant 4$ and $1 \leqslant y \leqslant 3\}$, $B = \{(x, y): x + y = 4\}$ and
$C = \{(x, y): x = 1\}$.
Find the value of $n(A)$ and the probability that a member of A chosen at random will also belong to
(a) the set B, (b) the set $B \cup C$.
(ii) Two white balls and six red balls were placed in a bag. A ball was taken at random from the bag, its colour was noted and the ball was replaced. A second ball was then drawn from the bag. Calculate the probability that the balls were
(a) both white, (b) both red, (c) of different colours. [C]

Answers

Exercise 1.1

1 (a) $5\frac{5}{12}$ (b) $\frac{13}{42}$ (c) $3\frac{1}{5}$ (d) $\frac{1}{6}$ (e) $\frac{64}{225}$ (f) 9   **2** £13·65   **3** (a) (i) 24·96
(ii) 25·0 (iii) 25 (b) (i) 0·108 (ii) 0·1 (iii) 0·11 (c) (i) 2·36 (ii) 2·4 (iii) 2·4
(d) (i) 14·88 (ii) 14·9 (iii) 15   **4** (a) (i) 0·42 (ii) 0·88 (b) $5\frac{6}{11}$ **5** (a) $\frac{39}{50}$,
(b) $1\frac{1}{40}$ (c) $\frac{1}{20}$ **6** $\frac{21}{25}$ by $\frac{1}{150}$ **7** (a) £6 (b) 250 g   **8** (a) 43·75 (b) 7·2
9 (a) £12 (b) $33\frac{1}{3}$ **10** £1·25   **11** 220 km/h   **12** 6·3 m   **13** £300, £400,
£1400   **14** 11:16:5   **15** (a) 14 (b) 0·14 (c) 2·8 (d) 0·0014   **16** 5
17 30   **18** 4·7   **19** (a) 6·5, 3·5; (b) 0, −2; (c) 1, $\frac{1}{2}$; (d) $2\frac{2}{3}$, $1\frac{1}{15}$ **20** 0·3
21 (a) $1·5 \times 10^5$ (b) $4·5 \times 10^{-2}$ (c) $2·58 \times 10^{-3}$ (d) $7·29 \times 10^{-4}$
22 (a) $1·62 \times 10^5$ (b) $3·64 \times 10^{-1}$ **23** smallest (a), largest (c)
24 20:13, 74%   **25** $1\frac{2}{3}$ **26** 8   **27** (a) £78 (b) 9·75   **28** 4·6 km/h; $4\frac{6}{11}$ km/h
29 (a) 64 (b) 40 (i) 132 (ii) 55   **30** 46 750

Exercise 1.2

1 $3\frac{4}{7}$ **2** (a) $\frac{5}{7}$ (b) 0·71   **3** (i) $\frac{7}{30}$ (ii) 207 000   **4** (i) $\frac{1}{12}$ (ii) 15·33   **5** 62
6 400   **7** (i) (a) 5 (b) 30·4 (ii) 40%   **8** (i) $\frac{4}{3}$ (ii) $\frac{4}{33}$ **9** 3·06   **10** 0·64
11 (a) $\frac{2}{3}$ (b) 4   **12** 30 450   **13** (i) 48 km/h (ii) £50   **14** £10·64
15 £40   **16** 7:10   **17** £120   **18** £178   **19** 40   **20** £1750   **21** 2
22 (a) £1360 (b) 32   **23** £2957·48   **24** 39 km/h   **25** $2·59 \times 10^{10}$
26 5×10^2 **27** 0·2   **28** (a) £13 200 000 (b) £4 125 000   **29** (i) £835 000
(ii) 10·4 (iii) £21 040 000; £12·70   **30** £5025, £4200, £675

Exercise 2.1

1 (i) £75 (ii) 625   **2** 75 cm   **3** 28 cm   **4** $1\frac{1}{2}$ cm^2 **5** 10, $n = 500 000$
6 (a) 240 (b) 30   **7** 1·21 km^2 **8** $\dfrac{39lb}{50}$, 22%   **9** $2(l+d)h$ m^2
10 1500 m^2 **11** 80 m, £75·60   **12** $\dfrac{60}{x^2}$ cm, $\left(4x^2 + \dfrac{360}{x}\right)$ cm^2
13 $r = 3\frac{1}{2}$ cm, $A = 38·5$ cm^2 **14** 9 cm   **15** 4 cm
16 88   **17** 8·15, 3·08   **18** $137\frac{1}{2}$ cm^3 **19** 105°
20 $24\frac{1}{2}$ cm^2, 14 cm^2 **21** 227   **22** 500   **23** (a) 149 760 cm^3 (b) 18 920 cm^2
24 (a) 2 (b) 10 m^2 **25** (i) 28 cm^2 (ii) 72   **26** 28   **27** 404 g (3 s.f.)
28 3 cm^3

Exercise 2.2

1 (i) 25 cm² (ii) 154 m **2** (a) 68 cm (b) 80 cm
3 (i) $\sqrt[3]{(3V/4\pi)}$ (ii) $10\frac{1}{2}$ cm **4** 15 197·6 cm³ 10·63 cm
5 (a) $17\frac{1}{2}$ cm (b) 393·75 cm², 12·5 cm² **6** (a) 140 m² (b) 52 m² (c) £31·20
7 (a) (i) 100 (ii) 10 (iii) 1000 (b) 5 cm **8** (i) $1\cdot5625 \times 10^{13}$ (ii) 4×10^{-5}
9 paved area = 68 m², volume = 45 m³; 9 hours
10 (a) 2411·52 cm³ (b) $V/\pi r^2$ (c) 3·185 cm **11** (a) 15 (b) 5
12 30 m³; $2\frac{1}{2}$ minutes; $4\frac{1}{2}$ m; $1\frac{1}{8}$ m **13** (i) 225:1 (ii) 125:1 (iii) 9:5
14 400; $r = \sqrt[3]{(3V/4\pi)}$; 1·44 mm; $1\cdot14 \times 10^{-4}$ mm
15 (a) 600 m (b) 27 (c) 100 (d) $130/x$ seconds (e) $130/x = 260 \Rightarrow x = \frac{1}{2}$

Exercise 3.1

1 (i) 17 (ii) 12 **2** (i) $\{1, 10\}$ (ii) $\{2, 3, 5, 7\}$ **3** (i) $\{2, 4\}$ (ii) $\{2, 3, 4, 5, 6, 7, 8\}$
4 (i) $M \cap W \neq \emptyset$ (ii) $C \subset W'$ (iii) $C \subset M$

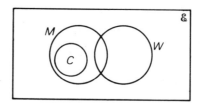

5 $\{1, 2, 4\}, \{1, 2, 8\}, \{2, 4, 8\}, \{1, 4, 8\}$ (i) $\frac{3}{4}$ (ii) $\frac{1}{2}$

6

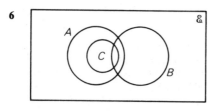

(a) $B \cap C = \{$multiples of 12 with two digits$\}$, e.g. 24
(b) $A' \cap C = \emptyset$
(c) $A \cup C = \{$even numbers with two digits$\}$ e.g. 14

7 (a) $R \cap P = R$ (b) 24 **8** (i) $\{6, 9, 12\}$ (ii) $\{5, 7, 11\}$
(iii) $\{5\}$ (iv) $\{9, 10, 11, 12\}$ (v) $\{4, 8\}$

9

×	−1	1
−1	1	−1
1	−1	1

$\{-1, 1\}$
identity = 1
$(-1)^{-1} = -1, 1^{-1} = 1$

×	−1	0	1
−1	1	0	−1
0	0	0	0
1	−1	0	1

$\{-1, 0, 1\}$
identity = 1
$(-1)^{-1} = -1, 1^{-1} = 1$

10

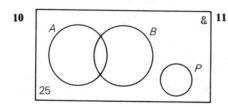

11

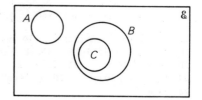

12 $\{a\}$ $\{b\}$ $\{c\}$ $\{a, b\}$ $\{b, c\}$ $\{a, c\}$ $\{a, b, c\}$ $\varnothing$

Exercise 3.2

1 $3x = 9 \Rightarrow x = 3$, number studying mathematics $= 16$

2 (i)

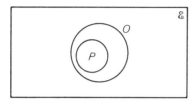 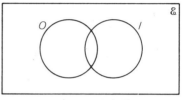

(a) $P \subset O$ (b) $O \cap I \neq \varnothing$

(c) there may not be a politician who is an idealist

(ii) (a) $\{3, 4, 5, 6, 7, 8\}$ (b) $\{0, 1, 2, 3, 4, 5, 6\}$

3 (i) e.g. square (ii) e.g.  (iii) e.g. isosceles trapezium (iv) e.g. kite

(a) $A \cap C = \varnothing$ (b) $B \cap A' \cap C \neq \varnothing$

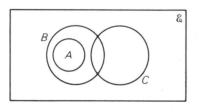

4

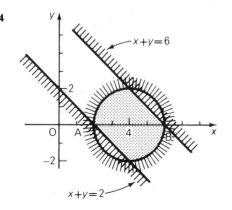

(i) P lies on or between the two lines $x + y = 6$ and $x + y = 2$

P lies on or inside the circle on diameter AB

(ii) Q lies in shaded region (including boundary lines); (2, 0), (3, 0), (3, 1), (3, −1), (4, 0), (4, 1), (4, 2), (4, −1), (4, −2), (5, 0), (5, 1), (5, −1), (6, 0); greatest distance = 4

5 (a)

⊕	0	1	2	3
0	0	1	2	3
1	1	2	3	0
2	2	3	0	1
3	3	0	1	2

(b)

⊗	1	3	7	9
1	1	3	7	9
3	3	9	1	7
7	7	1	9	3
9	9	7	3	1

(c) 0 ↔ 1 or 0 ↔ 1
    1 ↔ 3   1 ↔ 7
    2 ↔ 9   2 ↔ 9
    3 ↔ 7   3 ↔ 3

(i) 0 (ii) 2 (iii) 0, 2   (i) 1 (ii) 9

6 (a) 6 (b) 5 (c) $\{x:7 \leqslant x \leqslant 9\}$ (d) $\{y: 5 \leqslant y < 6\}$ (e) $\{2, 3\}$

*	1	2	3	4
1	1	1	2	2
2	1	2	2	3
3	2	2	3	3
4	2	3	3	4

$\{1, 2, 3, 4\}$ is closed under * as all entries in the table are members of the set.
As no row or column repeats the table headings, there is no identity, and hence no inverses.
A set of consecutive integers is closed under *.

Exercise 4.1

1 (a) 25 (b) 18 (c) 5   2 (a) $10nr$ (b) $\dfrac{1}{10}nr$; $r = \dfrac{80}{n}$ 3 $\dfrac{9v}{250}$ 4 $y = 8, b = 2,$

$c = -1 \cdot 55$ 5 $k = \dfrac{p + qr}{q^2}$ 6 $n\left(s - \dfrac{c}{10}\right)$ 7 $c = \dfrac{ab}{2a + b}$ 8 $\dfrac{-2y}{x(x - 2y)}$

9 $x(3x^2 - 5xy + 3y^2)$ 10 $\dfrac{-(2x + 15y)}{15}$ 11 $\dfrac{p}{q}$ 12 $d = \dfrac{7}{2}ut$; $26\tfrac{2}{3}$ km/h

13 (a) 7 (b) $\dfrac{1}{3}$ 14 $g = \dfrac{4\pi^2 a}{T^2}$; $1 \cdot 0$ 15 5   16 $(x + 7)(x - 7)$

17 $(x + 2)(x + 3)$ 18 $(x - 9)(x + 2)$ 19 $(2x + 5)(2x - 5)$ 20 $(x - 6)(x - 2)$
21 $(x + 6)(x - 3)$ 22 $(3x - 1)(2x - 5)$ 23 $2(x + 4)(x - 4)$ 24 $(2x - 1)(x + 4)$
25 $(10x + 7)(x - 2)$ 26 $x = 3$ 27 $x = -2$ 28 $x = \pm 4\tfrac{1}{2}$
29 $x = 4, 5$ 30 $x = -5, 7$ 31 $x = -4, -8$ 32 $x = -11, 7$

33 $x = -\tfrac{1}{2}, \tfrac{2}{3}$ 34 $x = 1\tfrac{1}{2}, 7$ 35 $x = -1\tfrac{1}{2}, -\tfrac{2}{5}$ 36 $1 \cdot 59, 4 \cdot 41$

37 $-9 \cdot 22, 0 \cdot 22$ 38 $-0 \cdot 85, 2 \cdot 35$ 39 $0 \cdot 31, 1 \cdot 29$ 40 $-1 \cdot 62, 0 \cdot 62$

41 $\{x:x \leqslant 4\}$ 42 $\left\{x:x > \dfrac{2}{5}\right\}$ 43 $\{x:x \leqslant -10\} \cup \{x:x \geqslant 10\}$

44 $\{x: -8 < x < 5\}$ 45 $\{x:x \leqslant 1\} \cup \{x:x \geqslant 3\}$ 46 (a) -1 (b) -4 (c) -6
47 (a) 21 (b) 147   48 $x = 2, y = -1$ 49 $x = -2, y = 4$
50 $x = 1\tfrac{1}{2}, y = -5$ 51 $x = 7, y = 3$ 52 $x = -3, y = -8$

53 $c = \dfrac{ab}{a - 2b}$ 54 $c = \dfrac{b(a - 1)}{1 + a}$ 55 $c = \dfrac{ab}{2 - b}$

Exercise 4.2

1 2   2 -17 3 5   4 -48 5 (i) $y = \dfrac{3}{4}$ (ii) $t = -4, 0$

6 $\{x:x < 1\}$;   7 (i) $x = 1 \cdot 5$ (ii) $2y + 7$ (iii) ± 6

8 $x = 1\tfrac{1}{2}$ 9 $x = -\tfrac{1}{2}$ 10 $\dfrac{1}{(x + 1)}$ 11 $\dfrac{3}{(x - 4)(x - 1)}$

12 (i) $\dfrac{2}{x(x + 2)}$ (ii) 7   13 (i) $6a^2$ (ii) $x = 35$ 14 $x = 7, y = -3$

15 (i) $x = 2, y = -1$ (ii) $8 - z$ **16** (a) $\dfrac{2}{3}$ (b) $p = 4, q = -1$ **17** (a) $x(x-7)(x+2)$

(b) $(a-2)(b-3c)$ **18** (a) $5(h+2k)(h-2k)$ (b) $(x-y)(x-y-3)$

19 (i) $(x+y)^2$ (ii) 19   **20** (i) (a) $2(p+3q)(p-3q)$ (b) $(r+s)(r+s+1)$

(ii) 0·57, 1·77   **21** (a) (i) $b(b-4)$ (ii) $(c+3)(c-3)$ (b) $y = \dfrac{2}{(x-1)}$ (c) (i) $(4n+1)(n+7)$

(ii) 401×107 **22** (i) $-2, \dfrac{3}{4}, 1$ (ii) 1   **23** (i) $(5x-11)(2x-1)$

(ii) $(2x+3y)(2x-3y)$ **24** $a = 10; (3x+5)$ **25** $x > -1$

26 (a) $x = 6$ (b) $x = 2, 9$ **27** (a) (i) $3(m-n)$ (ii) $m+n; m = 2\frac{1}{2}, n = 1\frac{1}{2}$

(b) (i) 7 m (ii) $\dfrac{1}{5}, 2$ **28** $-1, 2$ **29** (i) $8, \dfrac{1}{9}, 16$ (ii) 0.81, 3.69

30 $\dfrac{(8h^2 + 3d^2)}{3d}$ **31** (a) (i) x cm (ii) $\dfrac{9x}{10}$ cm (iii) 27·1 (b) 11 (c) (i) $(x+y)^2$

(ii) 63   **32** $x = 6\frac{1}{2}, y = -4\frac{1}{2}$ **33** (a) $x < 1$ (b) $-3 < x < 3;$ $\{x: -3 < x < 1\}$

34 $x = -1\frac{1}{3}, y = -\frac{2}{3}; x = 1\frac{1}{3}, y = \frac{2}{3}$ **35** (a) $\dfrac{5}{x-6}$, (b) $\dfrac{5}{x+6}$;

$\dfrac{5}{x-6} + \dfrac{5}{x+6} = 2 \Rightarrow x^2 - 5x - 36 = 0; x = 9;$ time $= 1$ h 40 min

Exercise 5.1

1 (i) $\{-3, 0, 5\}$ (ii) $\{0, 1, 3, 4\}$ **2** (a) (i) 14 (ii) 2 (iii) $\frac{1}{2}$ (iv) -4
(b) the real number line from -4 to 17   **3** $k = 9, x = \frac{1}{2}$ **4** (a) 4 (b) 8
5 (a) $A = 1, B = -2$ (b) h is 2–1, h' is 1–1   **6** (i) 28 (ii) 18 or 19 (iii) 30

7 (i) (a) $2, -1$ (b) $2, -1, \frac{1}{2}$ (c) $2, -1, \frac{1}{2}$ $(g = f^2)$ **8** gf: $x \rightarrow \dfrac{x^2}{4} + x;$

$\{x: -4 \leqslant x \leqslant 0\}$ **9** (i) $y = 3x$ (ii) 4   **10** $a = 2, b = -5;$ gradient $= 2\frac{1}{2}$
11 $k = 100, t = 11\frac{1}{5}$ **12** $k = 2$ **13** (i) $\frac{1}{2}$ (ii) $2y = x + 6$
14 (a) $(3, 5)$ (c) $2y = x - 2$ **15** $x \geqslant 0, y \geqslant -1, y \leqslant -x + 1, y \leqslant 0$

16

17 $6x - \dfrac{2}{x^3}$ **18** $y = 2x - \dfrac{1}{x} + 1$ **19** $y = x^2 - 5x + 3; y = -1$

21 54   **22** 9   **23** 500   **24** (i) $k = 7$ (ii) -2 (iii) minimum at $(2, 5)$
25 (i) 6 (ii) 36 cm (iii) 6 cm/s (iv) -6 cm/s^2

Exercise 5.2

1 (i) $f^{-1}: x \rightarrow x + 3$ (ii) $g^{-1}: x \rightarrow \pm\sqrt{x}$ (iii) gf: $x \rightarrow x^2 - 6x + 9$
(iv) fgf: $x \rightarrow x^2 - 6x + 6$ (v) $(gf)^{-1}: x \rightarrow \pm\sqrt{x+3}$ (vi) $(fgf)^{-1}: x \rightarrow 3 \pm\sqrt{(x+3)};$
h: $x \rightarrow x - 6;$ $(hgf)^{-1}: x \rightarrow 3 \pm\sqrt{(x+6)}; x = 0.17$ or 5·83

2 $fg: x \rightarrow (ax-2)^2$; $gf: x \rightarrow ax^2-2$; $a = 2 \Rightarrow x = 1, 3$, $fg < gf$ when $1 < x < 3$; when $a = 1$, $fg = gf \Rightarrow x = 1\frac{1}{2}$ **3** $gf: x \rightarrow 18x^2-24x+9$; $a = 1, b = 1$, $fgh(-2) = 7$; $x = 3, 1$ **4** (a) $-1, \frac{3}{4}$ (b) $-1 < x < \frac{3}{4}$
5 Area $= 33\frac{1}{3}$ (a) distance, metres (b) volume, cm^3
6 40, 20, 12·5, perimeter $= 2x + 2y$, values $= 17·3$ and $57·7$
7 $x = -2·58, 0·58$; $5x^2 + 4x - 17 = 0$; $x \approx -2·69, 1·09$
8 (a) acceleration; gradient $= 1\frac{1}{3}$ (b) 400 m (c) 24 m/s (d) 2000 m
9 $x^3 - 2x - 8 = 0$, $x = 2·93$ **10** (i) as percentage of large $\geqslant 0 \Rightarrow x + y \leqslant 100$
(ii) $x \geqslant 2y$ (a) $x = 33 - 33·5$ (b) 40 to 80 **11** (i) $y > x$ (ii) $y < 3x$
(iii) $x + y > 100$ (iv) $x + y < 140$ e.g. $x = 30, y = 80$
12 $y \leqslant \frac{3}{2} \Rightarrow 2y \leqslant 3x$; $2500x + 3500y \leqslant 35\,000 \Rightarrow 5x + 7y \leqslant 70$; $x \geqslant 3, x + y \leqslant 12$;
daily profit £$(2x + 3y)$ is maximised when $x = 7, y = 5$
13 x coordinate of R is $\sqrt{7}$; (1, 9), (2, 22) **14** $v = 3t^2 - 4t + 1$, $a = 6t - 4$
(a) $t = \frac{1}{3}$s, 1 s (b) $\frac{4}{27}$ m (c) $-\frac{1}{3}$ m/s **15** (i) $x = 27$ (ii) 36 (iii) $t = 4$ s (iv) 12
16 (a) $A = 1, B = 8$ (b) $x = -2$ (d) $x = 2\frac{1}{2}$ (e) 1·6 **17** area $1\frac{1}{3}$; volume $\dfrac{53\pi}{15}$
18 (a) (2, 0), (6, 0) and (0, -12) (b) (4, 4); area $= 10\frac{2}{3}$
19 minimum at (3, -4), maximum at (-1, 28); P is point (1, 12); Q is point (2, 0)
20 distance $= 54$ m ($0 \leqslant t \leqslant 3$); distance $= 94\frac{1}{2}$ m ($3 \leqslant t \leqslant 6$)

Exercise 6.1

1 129° **2** 156° **3** 63° **4** 8 **5** (a) 105° (b) largest side would be greater than the sum of the other two sides **6** 40 **7** angle Q $= 124°$, angles X and Y are 28° **8** 5, 6 **9** 45° **10** 40°, 140° **11** (a) Perpendicular bisector of XY (b) a pair of lines parallel to XY and distance 3 cm from XY **13** (b) and (c) **14** 7
16 7·416 cm ($\sqrt{55}$) **17** 78°, 46°, 92° **18** (i) 10 cm (ii) 124° **19** (i) 10·63 cm (ii) $\angle$BAE $= 100°$ **20** (i) $8\frac{3}{4}$ cm (ii) 12·65 cm (iii) 5:7 (iv) 16:49 **21** (i) a circle, centre P, radius 3 cm (ii) perpendicular bisector of QR (iii) angle bisector of $\angle$QPR **22** 43°, 43°, 82° **23** 17 cm, 8·485 cm **24** 36° **25** (i) 73° (ii) 135° (iii) $\angle$D $= 120°$, AB and DC (iv) 108° (opposite 72°) and 96° (v) 12 cm

Exercise 6.2

1 ($-4, 0$) **2** 28 square units **3** (i) (1, 9) (ii) (1, 3) (iii) (6, 1) **4** (a) a reflection in the line $x + y = 6$ (b) translation ($\frac{2}{1}$) (c) rotation, with centre ($4\frac{1}{2}, 2\frac{1}{2}$), through angle of 90° (anticlockwise) **5** (i) 15 (ii) 1:9 **6** R is the point ($4\frac{1}{2}, 4\frac{1}{2}$); point of intersection of perpendicular bisectors of AA' and BB' **7** (b) A'(3, 0), B'(9, 6), C'(6, 9) (c) A''(15, 9), B''(3, -3), C''(9, -9) (d) enlargement, scale factor $-\frac{1}{6}$, centre (3, $1\frac{1}{2}$)
8 P'($-3, -1$), Q'($-3, 1$) R'($-1, 1$), S'($-1, -1$); rotation about (2, 0) through 90° anticlockwise, coordinates of P'($-3, 1$); reflection in the line $x + y = 2$, P'($-3, -1$); translation ($\frac{-4}{-4}$), P'($-1, 1$)

Exercise 6.3

1 $\approx 5·05$ cm and 9·95 cm **3** YR ≈ 4 cm, PY $= 6·4$ cm **6** $r \approx 4·4$ cm
7 OA $\approx 2·9$ cm, BL $= 5$ cm

Exercise 7.1

1 (a) (i) $\begin{pmatrix} 4 & 5 \\ 0 & 7 \end{pmatrix}$ (ii) $\begin{pmatrix} 3 & 9 \\ 0 & 10 \end{pmatrix}$ (iii) $\begin{pmatrix} 3 & 11 \\ 0 & 10 \end{pmatrix}$ (b) $\begin{pmatrix} 1 & -\frac{1}{2} \\ 0 & \frac{1}{2} \end{pmatrix}$ **2** (a) $\begin{pmatrix} 10 & 0 \\ 4 & 7 \end{pmatrix}$
(b) (2 8) **3** (i) $\begin{pmatrix} 2 & 0 \\ 0 & 2 \end{pmatrix}$ (ii) $x = \frac{1}{2}, y = 1$ **4** $x = 10, y = 0$ **5** $A = \begin{pmatrix} 1 & 1 \\ 1 & 2 \end{pmatrix}$

$$\mathbf{B} = \begin{pmatrix} 4 & -1 \\ -1\frac{1}{2} & \frac{1}{2} \end{pmatrix}$$
  6 $c^2 + 4c - 12 = (c+6)(c-2); \ c = -6, +2$ **7** $\begin{pmatrix} 4 & -3 \\ -2\frac{1}{2} & 2 \end{pmatrix}$

8 $a = 2, b = 10$ **9** reflection in y-axis   **10** M: rotation of 90° anticlockwise about O; N: enlargement, centre O, scale factor 2; P: enlargement, centre O, scale factor 2, rotated through 45° anticlockwise about O.

11 $p = 2, q = -1$ **12** (a) $\begin{pmatrix} 7 \\ 0 \end{pmatrix}$ (b) $\begin{pmatrix} 5 \\ 12 \end{pmatrix}$ **13** (a) $\begin{pmatrix} 0 & 1 \\ 1 & 1 \end{pmatrix}$ (b) 25

14

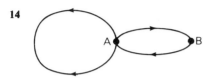

15 $\begin{pmatrix} 1 & -2 \\ 4 & 7 \end{pmatrix}$ **16** $x = -1, y = 3$ **17** $\begin{pmatrix} 14 & 2 \\ -3 & 0 \end{pmatrix}$ **18** $\begin{pmatrix} 6 & 10 & 4 \\ 8 & 5 & -3 \end{pmatrix}$; $A' = (6, 8)$,

$B' = (10, 5)$, $C' = (4, -3)$ **19** $(ac + bd), d = 7\frac{1}{2}$ $\begin{pmatrix} ca & cb \\ da & db \end{pmatrix}$,

determinant $= abcd - abcd = 0$ **20** $\begin{pmatrix} 7 & 0 \\ 0 & 7 \end{pmatrix}$

Exercise 7.2

1 $\mathbf{A}^2 = \begin{pmatrix} 1 & 0 \\ 6 & 1 \end{pmatrix}$, $\mathbf{B}^2 = \begin{pmatrix} 1 & 0 \\ 10 & 1 \end{pmatrix}$, $\mathbf{AB} = \begin{pmatrix} 1 & 0 \\ 8 & 1 \end{pmatrix}$, $\mathbf{XY} = \begin{pmatrix} 1 & 0 \\ x+y & 1 \end{pmatrix}$ (a) $\begin{pmatrix} 1 & 0 \\ 16 & 1 \end{pmatrix}$
(b) $\mathbf{A}^2\mathbf{B}$, $\mathbf{Q} = \mathbf{A}^3\mathbf{B}^2$ (c) $k = -5$ (d) $y = 2x - 2$

2 (i) $\begin{pmatrix} 2 & 2x \\ 3+y & 3x-1 \end{pmatrix}$ (ii) $x = 5, y = 4, z = 2, p = 3,$ (iii) $y = 3x$

3 (a) $\begin{pmatrix} 4 & -1 \\ 5 & 4 \end{pmatrix}$ (b) $\begin{pmatrix} 7 & 7 \\ 0 & 12 \end{pmatrix}$ (c) $\begin{pmatrix} 3 & 1 \\ 2 & 4 \end{pmatrix}$ (d) 30 (e) $x = 1, y = 1$

4 Determinant $= 1$ for all values of a (i) $\mathbf{M}^{-1} = \begin{pmatrix} a-1 & 1 \\ -a^2+a-1 & -a \end{pmatrix}$

(ii) $\mathbf{M}^2 = \begin{pmatrix} a-1 & 1 \\ -a^2+a-1 & -a \end{pmatrix} = \mathbf{M}^{-1}$

5 (a) (i) $\begin{pmatrix} 4 & 9 \\ 2 & 7 \end{pmatrix}$ (ii) $\begin{pmatrix} 12 & 3 \\ 6 & 9 \end{pmatrix}$ (iii) $\begin{pmatrix} 16 & 12 \\ 8 & 16 \end{pmatrix}$

(b) (i) $\begin{pmatrix} 1 & 0 \\ 0 & 1 \end{pmatrix}$ (ii) $\begin{pmatrix} 1 & 0 \\ 0 & 1 \end{pmatrix}$

6 (i) (a) $\mathbf{AB} = \begin{pmatrix} 1 & 0 \\ 0 & 1 \end{pmatrix}$, $\mathbf{BA} = \begin{pmatrix} -9 & 9 & 7 \\ -10 & 10 & 7 \\ 0 & 0 & 1 \end{pmatrix}$

(b) $\mathbf{ABA} = \begin{pmatrix} -4 & 4 & 3 \\ -1 & 1 & 1 \end{pmatrix}$, $\mathbf{BAB} = \begin{pmatrix} 2 & 1 \\ 3 & -2 \\ -1 & 4 \end{pmatrix}$

(c) **B** is not the inverse of **A**, $\mathbf{BA} \neq \mathbf{I}$; matrices must be square
(ii) $x = 19, y = 17$

7 (iii) enlargement, centre O, scale factor 2; (v) reflection in the line $y = 2x$
8 M represents a rotation, centre O, through angle 36° 52′ anticlockwise;

$\mathbf{MN} = \begin{pmatrix} 0 & -1 \\ 1 & 0 \end{pmatrix}$ represents a rotation of 90° anticlockwise about O;

N is a rotation, centre O, through angle 53° 8′ anticlockwise

9 M is an enlargement, centre O scale factor 5; equation of invariant line is $y = \frac{1}{4}x$; N is the enlargement followed by the reflection in the line $y = \frac{1}{3}x$

10 (a) (i) $\begin{pmatrix} 6 & 4 & 8 \\ 3 & 7 & 8 \end{pmatrix}$ (ii) (2600 3900) (iii) (70 200) (b) £702 (c) £842·40

11 (ii) rotation, centre O, through 90° anticlockwise
(iii) gradient = 2, equation: $y = 2x + 3$ (iv) $2y = -x - 3$
12 (ii) OA′ = 12, angle AOA′ = 36°52′ (iii) angle of rotation = 36°52′ anticlockwise; scale factor 3 (iv) area of O′A′B′C′ = 9 × 16 = 144 square units, A′C′ = 16·97 $(3 \times 4\sqrt{2})$

13 Not always true: (a) $\begin{pmatrix} 3 & 1 \\ 6 & 4 \end{pmatrix}\begin{pmatrix} 1 & 2 \\ 3 & 4 \end{pmatrix} \neq \begin{pmatrix} 1 & 2 \\ 3 & 4 \end{pmatrix}\begin{pmatrix} 3 & 1 \\ 6 & 4 \end{pmatrix}$;

(d) $\begin{pmatrix} 3 & 1 \\ 6 & 2 \end{pmatrix}\begin{pmatrix} 1 & 0 \\ -3 & 0 \end{pmatrix} = \begin{pmatrix} 0 & 0 \\ 0 & 0 \end{pmatrix}$
14 (a) (i) (3, 9) (ii) (14, 8) (iii) $2g + h + 3 = 0, -g + h + 9 = 0 \Rightarrow g = 2, h = -7$
(b) (i) −3 (ii) −1, scale factor 2

Exercise 8

1 P is the mid-point of AB, Q is the centroid of △AOB

2 (a) (i) $\begin{pmatrix} 10 \\ 20 \end{pmatrix}$ (ii) $\begin{pmatrix} 0 \\ -2 \end{pmatrix}$ (b) $\sqrt{5} = 2·236$ **3** $m = 3, n = -2$

4 $x = 17, y = 1\frac{1}{2}$ **5** $\mathbf{b} - \frac{1}{2}\mathbf{a}$ **6** (i) $\begin{pmatrix} 2 \\ 6 \end{pmatrix}$ (ii) $\begin{pmatrix} 7 \\ 6 \end{pmatrix}$ (iii) 5

7 $\begin{pmatrix} 6 \\ 4 \end{pmatrix}$ **8** $\overrightarrow{OD} = \frac{1}{2}(\mathbf{b} + \mathbf{c})$, $\overrightarrow{OG} = \frac{1}{3}(\mathbf{a} + \mathbf{b} + \mathbf{c})$

9 90° (diagonals of a rhombus) **10** $\overrightarrow{BC} = \begin{pmatrix} 2 \\ -4 \end{pmatrix}$, 68° **11** $m = 4, n = -6$

12 $\overrightarrow{AB} = \mathbf{b} - \mathbf{a}$, $\overrightarrow{BC} = -3\mathbf{a} - \mathbf{b}$, $\overrightarrow{AD} = -\mathbf{a} - 3\mathbf{b}$, $\overrightarrow{DC} = 3(\mathbf{b} - \mathbf{a})$;
$\overrightarrow{AB}$ and $\overrightarrow{DC}$ are parallel; an enlargement, centre O, scale factor −3
13 $\mathbf{a} + \mathbf{b} + \mathbf{c} + \mathbf{d} = 0$;
$\overrightarrow{WX} = \frac{1}{2}(\mathbf{a} + \mathbf{b})$, $\overrightarrow{ZY} = -\frac{1}{2}(\mathbf{c} + \mathbf{d})$ **14** $\mathbf{w} + \mathbf{a} = \mathbf{g}$; $|\mathbf{a}| : |\mathbf{g}| = 1 : \sqrt{2}$
15 (a) $\frac{1}{2}\mathbf{a} - \mathbf{b}$ (b) $\frac{1}{2}(\mathbf{a} - \mathbf{b})$ (c) $\frac{1}{2}h(\mathbf{a} + \mathbf{b})$ (d) $k(\frac{1}{2}\mathbf{a} - \mathbf{b})$ (f) $h - k = 0$,
$1 - \frac{1}{2}h - k = 0 \Rightarrow h = \frac{2}{3} = k$ **16** $\overrightarrow{BP} = \frac{1}{2}(\mathbf{b} - \mathbf{a})$, $\overrightarrow{AP} = \frac{1}{2}(\mathbf{a} + \mathbf{b})$, $\overrightarrow{AQ} = \frac{1}{4}(\mathbf{a} + \mathbf{b})$,
$\overrightarrow{BQ} = \frac{1}{4}(\mathbf{b} - 3\mathbf{a})$, $\overrightarrow{BR} = k\mathbf{b} - \mathbf{a}$; $k = \frac{1}{3}$, BQ:QR = 3:1 **17** $\overrightarrow{OC} = (\mathbf{a} + \mathbf{b})$,
$\overrightarrow{BD} = 2\mathbf{a} - \mathbf{b}$, $\overrightarrow{BP} = \mathbf{a} - \frac{1}{2}\mathbf{b}$, $\overrightarrow{PD} = \mathbf{a} - \frac{1}{2}\mathbf{b}$; P is the mid-point of BD; $\overrightarrow{BX} = \frac{1}{3}(2\mathbf{a} - \mathbf{b})$;
BX:XD = 1:2 **18** (i) $2\mathbf{n} + 2\mathbf{e}$ (ii) 2·828 km/h

19 $\overrightarrow{PR} = \mathbf{b} - \mathbf{a}$, $\overrightarrow{QS} = \frac{4}{3}\mathbf{b} - \frac{3}{2}\mathbf{a}$, $\overrightarrow{OX} = 4\mathbf{b} - 3\mathbf{a}$, $\overrightarrow{PX} = 4\mathbf{b} - 4\mathbf{a}$, $\overrightarrow{PX} = 4\overrightarrow{PR}$,
$\overrightarrow{PS} = -\mathbf{a} + \frac{4}{3}\mathbf{b} = \frac{1}{3}\overrightarrow{OX}$
20 (i) $\overrightarrow{MN} = 2\mathbf{b} - 3\mathbf{a}$ (ii) $\overrightarrow{MP} = \frac{1}{2}\mathbf{b} - \frac{3}{4}\mathbf{a}$ (iii) $\overrightarrow{BP} = 2\frac{1}{4}\mathbf{a} - \frac{1}{2}\mathbf{b}$, $|\mathbf{b} - \mathbf{a}| = 4$, $|\overrightarrow{MN}| = 8·54$

Exercise 9.1

1 (a) 2·89 cm (b) 5·35 cm (c) 14·3 cm (d) 9·95 cm (e) 11·5° (f) 33·7°

2 5 cm and 8·66 cm **3** 5 cm **4** (a) $\frac{y}{x}$ (b) $\frac{x}{\sqrt{(x^2 + y^2)}}$ (c) $\frac{x}{\sqrt{(x^2 + y^2)}}$
5 6·67 cm **6** 11·5°, 2·75 m **7** 10 cm; 73·7° and 106·3° **8** 1·73 cm
9 83·6°, 111·8°, 111·8°, 52·8°; AC = 12·5 cm **10** 0·165 cm or 19·8 cm **11** 9·51 cm
12 48·2 cm² **13** 1·33 km **14** 54·2 m **15** 9·33 cm (5 cos 30° + 10 sin 30°)
16 AG = 6·16 cm (a) ∠GAC = 18·9° (b) ∠GAH = 54·2°
(c) ∠AJD = 43·1° (d) ∠FAB = 21·8° **17** (a) 3·23 cm (b) 31·3° (c) 49·5°
(d) 45·8° (e) 11·1 cm (f) 65·2° or 114·8° (g) 46·6° or 133·4° (h) 9·16 cm
(i) 20·4 cm (j) 117·3° **18** (a) 8·39 cm (b) 137·3° (c) 27·5 cm²
19 (a) 41·4° (b) 9·92 cm² **20** 30° or 150°

Exercise 9.2

1 (i) 10·58 cm (ii) 82·82°   **2** (i) 44·92 cm (ii) 449·2 cm^2 **3** 92·26 m
4 197·05°   **5** (i) 3·356 cm (ii) 5·22 cm (iii) $\frac{1}{2}$ (iv) 5·29 cm   **6** 8·7 cm
7 (i) 26·05 cm (ii) area $\triangle$ PAB = 214·59 cm^2; area ABCD = 429·18 cm^2; AD = 17·17 cm;
area $\triangle$ QAD = 147·4 cm^2 **8** (a) 94·21 m (b) 316·75° (c) 0·655   **9** (a) 66·42°,
23·58° (b) 25 cm^2 **10** 61·04°   **11** (i) 7 cm (ii) 9 cm (iii) 48°

12 (i) $\frac{4}{5}$ (ii) 6 cm (iii) 16·8 cm^2 **13** 9·51 cm   **14** (a) 11·01 cm (b) 13·61 cm

(c) 38·66° (d) 52·29°   **15** (a) $\frac{12}{13}$ (b) $\frac{-5}{13}$ **16** $\cos \alpha = -\frac{15}{17}$, $\tan \alpha = -\frac{8}{15}$

17 (a) $\frac{12}{13}$ (b) $\frac{-12}{13}$ **18** (a) 108°, 252°, etc (b) (i) -14 (ii) 10·77 cm
19 11·82 cm   **20** XQ = 1·673 km, XR = 1·629 km, shortest distance = 1·572 m
21 $\angle$ RPQ = 75·52°, bearing = 014·45°, $\angle$ SPQ = 70°, $\angle$ SQP = 30°, PS = 3·05 km
22 (i) 7·211 cm (ii) 12·65 cm (iii) 31° (iv) 34·75°   **23** (a) 44·05° (b) 16·97 cm
(c) 66·13°   **24** (i) 98·13 m (ii) 48 m (iii) 333·93°, elevation = 34·82°
25 (i) 1130 m, 430 m (ii) 1210 m (iii) 291°

Exercise 10

1 (i) $\frac{1}{5}$ (ii) 100

2 (a) 3 (b) 2 (c) 23   **3** (i) Mid-values: 39, 41, 43, 46 (ii) 41·0
4 4, 14½; 4   **5** cows 72°, pigs 48°, sheep 150°, chickens 90°

6 (i) 4 (ii) 3 (iii) 3·41   **7** relative frequency = $\frac{1}{9}$, probability = $\frac{1}{3}$

8 (i) 3 (ii) 4 (iii) 4·2 (iv) 4   **9** 11   **10** (a) 5·14 (b) 6 (c) 4;

new mean = 6·1   **11** Median divides histogram so that areas on either side are equal

12 (i) median = 37, interquartile range = 11 (ii) (a) $\frac{1}{5}$ (b) $\frac{19}{60}$ (iii) $\frac{11}{295}$

13 (i) entries are 2, 2, 15, 16, 12, 2, 1
(ii) cumulative frequencies are 2, 4, 19, 35, 47, 49, 50
(iii) median = 6·76, lower quartile = 5·0, upper quartile $\approx$ 8·4
(iv) $\approx 47\%$

14 (i) $\frac{2}{3}$ (ii) $\frac{5}{9}$ **15** (a) (i) 4 (ii) 3 (iii) 3·2 (iv) $\frac{23}{50}$ (b) (i) $\frac{1}{12}$ (ii) $\frac{5}{12}$

16 (a) $\frac{3}{10}$ (b) $\frac{1}{15}$ (c) $\frac{8}{15}$ (d) $\frac{1}{45}$

17 (a) $\left\{\frac{2}{3},\frac{2}{5},\frac{2}{7},\frac{4}{3},\frac{4}{5},\frac{4}{7},\frac{6}{3},\frac{6}{5},\frac{6}{7}\right\}$ (i) $\frac{2}{7},\frac{2}{5}$ (ii) $\frac{6}{5},\frac{4}{3},\frac{6}{3}$; $p = \frac{5}{9}$ (b) (i) 6, $p = \frac{1}{2}$

(ii) (a) $\frac{1}{4}$ (b) $\frac{3}{16}$ **18** (a) $\frac{1}{6}$ (b) $\frac{3}{4}$ (c) $\frac{1}{12}$

19 (a) 9 (b) (i) $\frac{1}{5}$ (ii) $\frac{1}{15}$ **20** (i) 12 (a) $\frac{3}{12}$ (b) $\frac{5}{12}$ (ii) (a) $\frac{4}{64}$ (b) $\frac{36}{64}$ (c) $\frac{24}{64}$